T5-AVM-423

3 2109 00302 6813

DATE DUE

1985

Elements of Technical Report Writing

Elements of
Technical Report Writing

PAUL M. ZALL
Los Angeles State College

HARPER & BROTHERS, PUBLISHERS, NEW YORK

Library of Congress catalog card number: 62-8886

Contents

Contents

Foreword

In the second half of the Twentieth Century we are followed by reports from the cradle to the grave. It is short shrift to some to know that there is a recording angel even after that. In any case, some of us have come to live with reports and made our peace. Some are born report writers, others learn by writing reports, and still others have report writing thrust upon them whether they like it or not. When the Budget Director of the United States delivers his annual report to Congress he needs a truck to haul it. When a drowning man goes down for the third time he utters a report that is a model of efficiency: "Glub." And somewhere between those extremes are people writing reports every day and sometimes into the night. Because reports are necessary, however, does not mean that they are necessarily evil. In fact, this book is dedicated to the proposition that there are elements of report writing that can do some good. Our purpose here is to offer the occasional report writer sympathetic understanding so that he may stamp out evil wherever he finds it in the report he has to write.

We are going to talk about writing reports in terms of the more common problems faced by the student or professional man who is not a writer by training or inclination, but finds himself having to write a report as part of a larger job. We will concentrate on "technical" reports because these are basic in form and style to reports in various fields such as commerce, insurance, or government service. But the technicality of the reports we will use as examples or for practice problems is at a fairly low level and we will avoid such specialties as writing for technical journals, industrial manuals, or government specifications.

The examples in the text and the practice problems following each section are drawn about equally from the classroom and industry. Except in the first chapter, no answers are provided for the practice problems because their solutions depend almost entirely upon the point-of-view and circumstances of individual writers. The purpose of the problems is to provide painless practice of some of the principles discussed in the text. The principle of solution is the important thing, and that is what we will be talking about.

We will discuss the various principles governing report writing in a sequence that parallels the steps a writer normally takes as he goes about a report writing project. The text can thus be read in order or used simply for reference and reminder. The first chapter ought to be read first, however, because it explains some of the assumptions upon which later chapters are based. Then in sequence we will talk about planning, collecting information, designing (outlining and organizing the over-all design), rough drafting, and revision. The chapter on proofreading and the recommended reading are mostly for quick and easy reference.

To thank everybody who helped compile this mass of material would double its size. Some are old students at UCLA, Los Angeles State College, and the University of Washington. With one or two exceptions, duly noted, they would probably prefer to remain anonymous. Friends and family helped, too, and so did colleagues at Boeing Airplane Company (Seattle), Northrop Corporation (Hawthorne, California), and the Communication Research Center at Los Angeles State College: chiefly Chris Christopherson and Hank Moore. But the real heroes of the text are those anonymous writers whose immortal words float around campus and industry in a variety of versions. Some of the best are preserved in Chapter 8 as well as throughout the text. There is no way now of finding the original authors. They are like the tombstones in New England churchyards saying: "Reader as thou passeth by, as you are now so once was I. . . ." We can profit from their errors or good sense, as the case may be, and feel a little better for knowing that they have been down this road before.

PAUL M. ZALL

Elements of Technical Report Writing

CHAPTER 1

Introduction

WHAT IS WRITING?

Since this is a book about writing, we had better begin by asking what writing is. For our purpose, it is the process of defining what we mean to say accurately and without ambiguity. Consider the difference between writing and speaking in this respect: we can easily understand what a man who is speaking *means to say* even though *what he says* does not make sense. The classic example of this is the young lady in the restaurant who was being annoyed by a young man and said: "If you don't stop bothering me, I'll go out and get somebody who will." In the same way, a speaker on the spot can say whatever comes to mind and then by means of gestures or other action or further speaking set right any misunderstanding. He can be relatively certain that he will be understood eventually.

Not so a writer. He has to think before he writes. He has to think as he is writing and also after he has written, not only to make sure that he will be understood but to guard against being misunderstood. The problem is that writing is a presentation of our thinking. But thinking is not always logically organized and connected. It comes in general, vague ideas or scattered bits of impressions. If we put our thoughts on paper as they came, they would be like the speech of the girl in the restaurant but without benefit of her "context," or the circumstances in which her words were spoken. For it was the context, not her words, that made her meaning clear. Unless we can convey the context

1

of our thinking, we are at a great disadvantage compared to her.

But writing does have one great advantage over speaking: it enables us to proceed by trial and error until we can formulate our ideas and parts of ideas in their best possible shape. That is why it is so often helpful to write something down just to see what it looks like. We can then see the whole of an idea and what its parts are, or the parts of an idea and what they add up to. Then we can distinguish between ideas or juggle the parts until we find the best order, the best arrangement, the best connection—and maybe even the best words—that accurately present what we mean to say. We can at least get them straightened out to our own satisfaction.

Much of the writing process, then, is a personal thing. For many people it is simply a means of "self-expression," or getting something off their minds or souls, as the case may be. But the moment we start writing to somebody else, we have to contend with the problem of context again. But here we have an unlooked-for advantage. Writing, after all, is not natural in the way speaking is natural. Writing is more artificial, more regulated by generally accepted conventions or ground-rules. Some of these conventions are so familiar that they themselves establish the context we need. Years of reading the newspapers, for example, lead us to expect to learn about "who," "what," "when," "where," and "how" in short order. In the same way, readers of reports expect to learn what you have to say in terms of: "What are you talking about?" "For instance?" "So what?" These questions establish the context of reports and most informative writing.

The writing process is geared to meet the context in which reports are read: in defining what we are talking about, we actually classify our ideas, separating one from another, the important from the unimportant, distinguishing one from others like it. In giving instances or examples, we actually analyze our ideas into their parts, showing how they are related to each other and to the whole subject, and also how they work together as a system. And, finally, in explaining the significance of what we have been talking about, we reclassify or restate our ideas in the light of the analysis. These steps have been repeated since at least the time of the ancient Greeks. They are taught in school and expected as a matter of course in college and professional life. We have a ready-made context.

But the trouble with writing is people. People's ideas about writing have caused no end of confusion for those who have to write. What happens is that readers tend to judge all writing by standards such as the prose of Faulkner or *Time* magazine or Winston Churchill. They do not realize that Faulkner, *Time* writers, and Sir Winston are all working in different contexts. We would laugh if Faulkner tried to write like Sir Winston and Sir Winston tried to write like the editors of *Time, Newsweek,* or *Mad Magazine.* We would laugh because their writing that way would be inappropriate. It would upset our expectations that have been established by familiarity.

Writing, in the sense that we are going to talk about it, consists of satisfying a report reader's expectations in three areas: subject matter, expression, and arrangement of materials. The governing factor is appropriateness.

WHAT IS APPROPRIATENESS?

Appropriateness is what Mark Twain had in mind when he wrote about the gentleman who, when asked what he thought about a woman using cuss words, replied: "She may know the words but she don't know the music." Appropriateness is the music of writing—knowing when to say something and how to say it for best effect. Now, most people with common sense use language appropriately, almost without thinking about it. For example, few people would use the language of church services when in a tavern. Few people would use the same language when applying for a job as they would when quitting one. The fact is people generally have a variety of languages at their disposal. Which language they use upon which occasion is determined by a sense of appropriateness.

We develop a sense of appropriateness in the same way that we develop good table manners—by self-control. Self-control, however, is usually a function of self-confidence, and this is why appropriateness in writing seems so hard for many people: they lack self-confidence. If a man is tongue-tied in public, it is usually because he is tongue-tied in private, too. He has nothing to say. But a man who has something to say and is convinced it is worth saying should have no problem. What he will usually do, however, is begin thinking about how he never did very well in English. Then he starts looking through the files to see what has been acceptable in the past. Or he looks for books, hoping for models he can follow—preferably with minimum change of wording. The result is chaos and confusion, all because he never stopped to consider that he is probably the best man to tell his story. He knows his subject. He knows his readers. He knows what they want to know and why they want to know it. Nobody else could provide these clues to appropriate writing.

APPROPRIATE REPORT WRITING

Self-confidence and thus self-control and thus appropriateness are nowhere more important than in report writing. However, most report writers have not been trained to write reports, and they confuse this kind of writing with other kinds of writing such as fiction or journalism. This confusion makes a tough job even tougher and results in completely inappropriate reports. So let us make some distinctions.

Functional

Report writing is intended to serve only its purpose of providing useful information—whether for immediate use, for later reference, or for permanent record. There is no intention to amuse or entertain. In fact, an amusing piece of writing would probably be tossed out as unprofessional. Report writing is essentially a commercial, industrial, or military activity, and it costs money. For amusement, management hires professional entertainers. For information and recommendations, they hire professional experts like you. The report tells them what you think they ought to know, gives them a basis for decision in facts and figures, and provides summaries and interpretations. That's what they're paying you for.

Informative

Reports are very different from "creative" or imaginative literature such as novels and short stories. One characteristic of "literature" is that it *suggests* the writer's message rather than *tells* it outright. Consider, for example, these versions of a familiar rhyme—one as we all know it, the other as it would have to be written in a report:

Humpty Dumpty sat on a wall;	Humpty Dumpty sat on a wall;
Humpty Dumpty had a great fall;	Humpty Dumpty had a great fall;
All the King's horses	All the King's horses
And all the King's men	And all the King's men
Couldn't put Humpty together again.	Couldn't put Humpty together again Because he was an egg.

This difference between *suggesting* and *telling* is the difference between letting the reader interpret what you mean and allowing him no room for interpretation other than what you intend. A practiced reader may interpret literature on several different levels of meaning. Reports try to limit interpretation to one literal, accurate meaning.

Factual

Literature also differs from reports in that it is concerned primarily with the dramatic rather than the factual elements in life. This is true of news stories as well. Even though newspapers are devoted to reporting facts and events as matters of record, they nevertheless are at the mercy of their readers and must therefore emphasize "human interest." This emphasis results in distortion—either by outright slanting or by oversimplification. The news writer must often oversimplify a complex subject so it will be understandable and present it in "cute" language so it will be readable by a housewife anywhere. But the report writer cannot do this. He must summarize, simplify, emphasize, but he must avoid distorting his information. If he distorts, he commits professional suicide.

Efficient

Because reports are professional as well as commercial activities, they must be efficient, as efficiency is defined in physics—they must do the job they are designed to do with minimum effort. Since the job they are designed to do consists of communicating information, reports must have a neat balance between brevity and thoroughness. A report writer, therefore, must know when he has said enough or not enough to suit his purpose. He must know his readers sufficiently well to realize how much introduction to the subject they need, how much preparation for what is to come. He must know also how to pace his presentation for them, giving just the right amount of information at a time to ensure understanding as well as easy reading. And he must be master of his material, knowing what to throw out, what to amplify, what to rewrite.

Preconceived Design

It is not enough for the report writer to say what he has to say, even if he has said it most efficiently. He must also present his information in such a way that it can be easily used for its purpose. In doing so, he might employ such devices as headings, indentations, illustrations, cross-references, tabulations, and so forth. He also should use standard mechanics, such as proper abbreviations and symbols, conventional spelling and punctuation. But chiefly he should use standardized formats—or patterns of organization—that enable practiced readers to find what they want in a hurry. The repetition involved in using these formats may seem to contradict the requirement of efficiency, but this kind of repetition is designed to increase usability rather than to enhance readability.

WHAT IS A REPORT?

A report is designed to fulfill a need to tell and a need to know by communicating a set of ideas from a writer's mind to a reader's mind. In a technical report the ideas will be ideas *of* things and ideas *about* things; i.e., data and interpretation. And these ideas will be presented in an easily understood pattern of organization with strong internal connections, proper balance, and appropriate expression. The form, proportions, and arrangement of parts will be governed by requirements of subject, audience, and purpose. These are the bases of structural integrity or appropriateness. Given a good foundation, a report writer can easily plan the sequence, arrangement, and connections of his ideas—making his point and getting it across.

We will be talking chiefly about technical reports. These differ from business reports in that in science and engineering the need to tell and the need to know are more urgent than the need to "sell" or "motivate" or impress one's boss, customer, or competitor. Since the emphasis is on the information rather than the expression, techniques of communication must be cut to the minimum and rigidly controlled. This is perhaps why so many readers find technical reports dull. Scientists and engineers do not like to write them either, and much prefer to communicate by means of formulas and drawings. But just as a bridge is more useful than a line on a map representing a bridge, so a report is more useful than a collection of raw data, labels, and tables. If reports must be dull, that does not mean that they cannot be both good and dull.

THE ABC'S OF REPORT WRITING

The requirements of appropriateness in report writing have many corollaries, and they will be discussed later in proper sequence throughout the book. But for purposes of a general view of report writing problems, they can be summarized here in the form of ABC's.

Accuracy

Months, years of labor may be made worthless because of a misplaced decimal point or misstated fact. One error in calculation, one illogical statement can cast a shadow of doubt over your whole report. You must therefore guard against sloppy thinking, careless calculation, and slipshod expression. Check every statement in its final form, because a statement that says one thing when it stands by itself may say something completely different when surrounded by other statements. Take care also in changing words in your text, for often one small change can change the meaning of an entire sentence, a whole paragraph— even a whole report. Accuracy of statement depends not only on individual words, but on the way sentences are put together, the way paragraphs are developed, and the way the report as a whole is balanced. As a rule, then, do not be content with being understood, but always guard against being misunderstood.

Brevity

Being brief is a courtesy to the reader. It is also a means of checking the development of your own ideas and the accuracy of your expression. From your reader's point of view, both features are to his advantage because he can get the essence of your thinking in compressed form. He is reading your report because (1) he has to as part of his job, or (2) he is looking for something. In either case, he would prefer to have your message handed to him in a well-wrapped, easy-to-handle package made as small as possible. So you begin with your main point and then show why it is sound. You emphasize the highlights of your work, cut out irrelevant comments, immaterial excursions, and meaningless statements. What you have left is the sum total of your information, which enables you—as well as your reader—to see what it all adds up to.

Confidence

When you finish the last page of your report you are an authority. You probably know more about the particular subject than anyone else at that time. You will have spent months compiling information, thinking about it, testing it, and constructing it into an orderly, connected body of thought. There is no reason, then, why you should hide behind a mass of "perhaps's" and "maybe's" or the many other forms of hedging. Lack of boldness is the cause of more beating about the bush than anything else since the invention of the fig leaf. If you are convinced that what you are saying is right and wise, say it—and let the chips fall where they may. If you are not convinced of the rightness and wisdom of what you are saying—then go back to see where the problem lies and how you can rectify it. More often than not, when a report is bad it is because the planning is bad.

Dignity

With confidence will come the ring of authority—dignity. Dignity is a courtesy to your readers as professional people. Some books on business-writing tell you to "write the way you talk." However, this is poor advice for report writers. In report writing, you will need formality with respect to words and the way words are used. Grammatical constructions should be complete; there should be no shortcuts. Pronouns such as "which" or "that" are used for clarity. Contractions like "can't" or "don't" should not be used. Diction must be exact, not flowery like "lovely," "definitely," or "quite." You must actually write better than you talk, and avoid such colloquial expressions as "try and" when you mean "try to." You will achieve simple dignity with straightforward expression, with summarized, simplified, and well-organized information.

Emphasis

It is possible for a report to have all the information and say all the right things but still not be good. A report that lacks properly placed emphasis will make everything seem as important as everything else. There will be no discrimination between the main point and subordinate points, between points and illustrations or examples, between the trees and the woods. You have to tell the reader what is important, and not expect him to find it out for himself. He will get lost. You have to lead him from point to point, clearly marking every step of the way and showing him where he is going and why you have stopped at a particular place. A straightforward style, plenty of guideposts, and frequent helping hands in the form of transitions will tell him where he is, where he has been, where he is going, and why the trip is worthwhile.

Facility

What makes writing easy to read? Short familiar words and short sentences are very helpful, but this kind of writing can easily become childish and unprofessional. Moreover, simple sentences cannot convey the logical forms of complex thinking often required in a report. Therefore, report writing depends more on pacing, sequence, arrangement, and connections to achieve smooth-flowing, easy-to-read continuity. (1) Pacing—technical or unfamiliar information should be presented in small segments and explained, defined, or otherwise illustrated before more of such information is presented. (2) Sequence—the reader should be led from the familiar to the unfamiliar, from the simple to the complex, from the whole to the parts. (3) Arrangement—the important parts should be emphasized and balanced to show their proper relationship and importance. (4) Continuity—the relation of one part to another should be clearly stated, illustrated, and emphasized.

Grammatical Correctness

Acceptable grammatical practice is important for sensible as well as social reasons. People have learned grammatical rules and expect others to use them too. If you upset their expectations they will feel uncomfortable and probably will be confused as well. Make your writing straightforward, logical, and clear and check your statements for sound as well as sense. Be sure to follow the basic rules of grammar.

Honesty

Honesty is expected in a report as a matter of course. The use of other people's information or work must be acknowledged, either in footnotes or in text. Honesty also involves reporting your own failures as well as successes, your own mistakes. This will then prevent some other researcher from making the same mistakes, and often it will provide a clue for some other researcher working on your problem from a different angle. The writer who glosses over his own mistakes or failures is doing no one any good and may do himself as well as others a lot of harm.

Illustration

Illustrative material, such as charts, graphs, diagrams, and photos, is always helpful. You should use them to clarify or support the text, not for their own sake. They can be used to summarize detailed and complex data or to simplify a complicated concept. They can be used to show a situation, a trend, or a movement. For whatever purpose they are used, they should be referred to somewhere in the text and should bear a caption referring directly to the discussion they are supporting. They ought to be fully and clearly labeled so that they can be understood at a glance.

Judgment

Judicious weighing of evidence is as important in a report as in a law court and the principles are the same for both. The best evidence is that which is (1) most ample; (2) most pertinent; (3) most simple in explaining the facts with least additional evidence; (4) most in harmony with the rest of the available evidence. In every case, the evidence used as a basis for judgment (as in conclusions or recommendations) should be included in the report.

Knowledge

The communication of knowledge is one of the chief functions of the report. But knowledge is more than a collection of data, for it involves interpretation and the formulation of conclusions. Without intelligent interpretation, data may well remain useless. The man in the best position to do the necessary interpreting is the man who has done the working and thinking. His thinking has been based on certain assumptions—laws or common sense—and these have guided his work. Someone else may apply entirely different assumptions and reach entirely different conclusions. So it is necessary to explain the basis of your work and put it into proper perspective. This may give the reader a chance to see old things in a new way or new things in a clear way. Either way, he will have gained knowledge which only you can give.

Logic

Thinking straight is so essential that it seems almost unnecessary to mention it. But as a reminder: logic is a process of showing the relations among groups of things and classes of groups.

It is chiefly a process of classification, putting things in their proper places. Thus, there are certain trouble spots to avoid: (1) statements must not contradict each other; (2) words must be used in a consistent sense; (3) statements must move in one direction, whether space, time, or relation; (4) statements must make sense; (5) judgments must not be based on too few data; (6) cause and effect should be clearly distinguished from simple sequence; (7) conclusions should not be inferred if they have no connection with the data; (8) an authority should not be accepted if he is biased, not an expert in the particular field, or not in a position to know the facts.

Mechanical Neatness

To make the best impression, a report should be in perfect shape. If it is neatly typed and well margined, a report is easier to read. Frequent headings, subheadings, and indentations are mechanical devices which help to make the organization of the content clear. As a courtesy, your report should also be free from typographical errors, crossings-out, smudges, and the like. A clean report shows that you cared enough to send the very best.

Normal Procedure

Conformity to standard practices makes a report easier to understand. People who read reports are used to finding certain things presented in standard fashion. If you depart from standard procedure, consider whether the risk is worth the assertion of your independence. The reader may find it confusing and unnerving and may be immediately unsympathetic no matter how good the material is. This is not to say that the standard way is always the best way, but if you want to change standard procedure you must re-educate the reader. If this is ever necessary, you can always devote a large part of your introduction to telling why you are doing something radical, giving sound reasons for doing so.

Objectivity

Being objective is hard for the beginning writer unless he can imagine himself as another person, an uninterested observer, or an innocent bystander. Then he can write about his work as if he were a man from Mars giving an unbiased report of what is going on down on Earth. It is not easy to restrain your emotions when writing about your own work. That is why you must pretend to be someone else and try to get yourself out of the picture. Commonly, reports avoid the use of the first person (I, me, my) in order to give the impression that the work being reported is a team effort or a company (rather than an individual) activity. Another reason for avoiding the first person is to give the reader the impression that there is no one standing between him and the work being reported.

Planning

The complete report writing project requires planning. It is here that most writers go astray. They think report writing is just a matter of sitting down with a piece of paper and scratching a few words of wisdom on it. But what you see in a report is what you see of an iceberg: the unseen part may be much greater than what is immediately visible. You ought to spend at least as much time planning as writing. You ought to have a clear idea of where you are going to end before you begin writing. You ought to have figured out on paper what you are going to talk about, why, how, and possibly where and when. Good planning will be repaid in time saved and nerves calmed. It will be reflected in an exact, descriptive title; a well-balanced table of contents; a clear and concise summary or abstract; and a well-organized report. Planning pays.

Qualification

You are required to explain the circumstances surrounding your work because they might have affected the results you are reporting. Modern scientific thinking is based on the concept of change—what is true at a given instant may no longer be true when that instant has passed. Thus, as you report your results, you are saying: "This is true under the given conditions." The scientific reader wants to know what these conditions were, not only because he would like to be able to reproduce them but because he would like to decide for himself whether your work is valid or not. This does not mean that you have to back and fill by qualifying everything you say. On the contrary, you must be bold and straightforward. But try to describe what factors were constant and what factors were variable as you worked. Try to describe them in such a way that the reader can see the circumstances.

Revision

Four phases in report writing are planning, designing, rough drafting, revising. Revising is the most important as far as expression is concerned. Planning, as noted above, is basic. Designing consists of organizing and arranging your data in logical form and appropriate format. Rough drafting consists of developing your ideas on paper. In the revision phase, all these things are reviewed and polished to perfection. The process of revision consists of more than merely correcting spelling or punctuation errors. You must check every statement for sense and relevance, and see whether you have said all that must be said—and not too much. It is best to review and revise some days after writing when you can take an objective view. Then, in the position of someone reading it for the first time, you can ask yourself how the report looks, how it reads, whether it makes sense, and whether it is right.

Straight Sentences

Sentences carry the full weight of meaning in a report. In a good report, each paragraph begins with a straightforward statement of its subject (topic sentence). Each sentence in the paragraph then has direct bearing on the first one. All sentences proceed straight ahead: generally the subject comes first and then the verb—you tell what you are talking about and then what you want to say about it. It is a good idea to limit a sentence to one idea or to two closely related ideas. The reader can thus grasp your meaning more easily than if you piled up idea upon idea. Transitions from sentence to sentence will show the reader how to follow your thought and also provide straightforward movement leading him where you want him to go. Variety of sentence structure can be effective for rounding off a point or for emphasis, but the chief thing to strive for is movement so that the sentences move straight ahead.

Thoroughness

Treat your subject fully if you want your report to have lasting value. On choosing a subject you are making a contract to provide thorough treatment of it. Thoroughness extends throughout the report writing project—from initial thinking to final submittal. You are therefore obligated to think through the subject, analyze and investigate it, analyze and organize the results, present your information, and draw significant conclusions—negative as well as positive. Make sure that you have said enough to satisfy the needs of your readers and your purpose. You can do this by (1) preparing a checklist of requirements in the planning phase, (2) marking off each requirement as it is fulfilled, and (3) using the checklist again in the revision phase for a final recheck.

Unity

A unified report is one in which everything is clearly relevant to the main point under discussion. Nothing should be left hanging—no questions left unanswered. One way to check unity is to read critically as you go along, asking "What has this to do with the subject?" Another more mechanical check is to draw a line from the subject of a paragraph to the subject of the next and succeeding paragraphs. If the subjects can be tied together, the report is probably unified. A third check is to prepare captions or headings for each paragraph and then list them in outline form. If they all bear directly on the title, chances are the report is unified. The effect of a unified report is to make the reader feel satisfied that he has read all that has had to be said.

Viewpoint

A report is written from a certain viewpoint—that of a reporter, teacher, researcher, or the like. The viewpoint is established with the first sentence and should be maintained consistently throughout the report. Thus the reader will get accustomed to hearing one voice. If you switch voices on him, he will feel something is wrong. So if you begin talking like a professor, stick with that voice to the bitter end. Be particularly careful about shifting viewpoint in the middle of a sentence.

Word Choice

A specialist finds it easy to talk to other specialists, for they speak the same language. Your report may be read by nonspecialists as well as specialists in your field, but it is safe to assume that this nonspecialist is at least a semispecialist, or he would not be reading your report. The semispecialist will have sense enough to grasp the meaning of specialized words from the context or he will look them up in a technical dictionary. There is no reason to avoid technical words in a technical report. There is good reason, however, to avoid pompous, ornate words, and especially vague words. Be as precise as you can: if you mean 24 samples say "24 samples" and not "a couple of dozen." If you mean the part could not be used because it rusted, say "The part was rusted beyond use," rather than "The part was not used due to rust."

You-Point

A report is not written to its writer. It is aimed at an audience, and so you should think in terms of pacing and timing. Thus your information can be presented in segments appropriate to your readers' knowledge and needs. Get into the habit of going from the simple to the complex, from the known to the unknown, the familiar to the unfamiliar, the nontechnical to the technical. And try to time the presentation so that readers have time to digest a complex bit of information. Allow for explanations in proportion to the complexity of the information, and allow for time to think about what you have just told them. Do not smother the readers with details, but show them the main ideas occasionally. Above all, avoid overwriting. Stop when you have said what needs to be said—but make sure you have said it.

Zest

Write only when you have something worth saying, and then write as though you were performing a service that only you can perform. Moreover, write as though you enjoyed it. If you get tired or bored, take a break, go for a walk, read a book, get some sleep. If you are bored writing a report, imagine how your readers will feel reading it. If you are sick of revising it, imagine how you will feel rereading it six months from now and seeing stupid mistakes. It may not be easy to think and work, but it need not be painful.

PRACTICE PROBLEMS: APPROPRIATENESS

1. Test your sense of appropriateness by evaluating the following report according to your own standards of report writing:

WASHINGTON SIGHTING, JULY, 1952[1]

On July 20, 1952, over Washington, D.C., a group of UFO's were tracked by the radar center at Andrews Field Air Force Base, the Radar Center at Washington, and the Local Control Center at Washington. The objects were plotted simultaneously by the three radar stations and it was realized that they were taking surprising liberties with the laws of mechanics. At one moment, one of the objects changed direction at an angle of 90 degrees without decelerating or describing any perceptible curve. A little later, another of the objects, also without noticeable deceleration, made a turn of 180 degrees. This means that at a speed of nearly 130 mph it suddenly reversed its course.

A jet plane piloted by Lieutenant William L. Patterson was passing over Washington at the time. He sighted one of the objects and headed straight for it at over 600 mph. As he approached the hovering object, it suddenly darted away from him and was tracked on radar at a speed in excess of 7000 mph.

An investigation by Major Donald E. Keyhoe, USMC Retired, Director of NICAP, revealed that a temperature inversion of 9 to 18 degrees Fahrenheit could have produced the results seen on the three radar scopes. However, Major Norman S. Lewis of the Westinghouse Weather Bureau, who is a specialist on temperature inversion, produced weather graphs which proved that the inversion on July 20 over Washington never exceeded one degree Fahren-

[1] Information for this report has been gathered from books on unidentified flying objects and publications of the National Investigations Committee on Aerial Phenomena (NICAP).

heit. The Air Force has officially labeled this sighting as being caused by temperature inversion.

2. What possible functions might be served by the reports from which the following excerpts have been drawn?

A. A main feature of the new laboratory is a strongback—a wall-like structure towering above surrounding test equipment. It looks big, even when viewed in the 23,000-square-foot laboratory. The strongback has muscle enough to hold the wing or fuselage of a B-52 global bomber by one end only, leaving the entire length freely suspended for test loading. It is built like an iceberg. Concrete and steel in the foundation alone weigh 2 million pounds. Up to 11 feet thick, the foundation rests on 196 piles driven deep in the earth. Above the floor, the strongback is 40 feet wide, 25 feet high and 8½ feet thick.

B. Dispensing with blading, the weakest element of a conventional turbine, the Tesla turbine has a rotor of closely spaced smooth discs to which energy is imparted by drag properties of fluid flow along logarithmic spiral stream lines. Notwithstanding its desirable characteristics, however, it has not been developed commercially because the inherently high rotational speed imposed restrictions on its initial application and construction.

C. A composite inventory of the Division's computer facilities reveals a solid acre of these machines with leases and purchases running to more than $2 million a year. Over the hum of fans which suck away the electronically generated heat, these computers chatter and spew out miles of tape and printed data 24 hours a day to keep up with the demands of our Accounting people.

D. The King ordered a tailor to come next morning, and take my measure for a suit of clothes. This operator did his office after a different manner from those of his trade in Europe. He first took my altitude by a quadrant, and then with a rule and compasses described the dimensions and outlines of my whole body, all which he entered upon paper, and in six days brought my clothes very ill made, and quite out of shape, by happening to mistake a figure in the calculation.

E. How contain a reaction occurring at temperatures of 10^8 degrees at which every refractory is not only vaporized but atom-ized and stripped down to its individual nuclei? Container there must be, for the reaction initially will be studied at pressures of the order of a ten-millionth of an atmosphere. The containers must therefore be vacuum-tight. What is equally certain is that the reaction zone, at its temperature of 10^8 degrees, must never be allow to impinge on the container walls—otherwise these latter would "go up in smoke," an atomic or nuclear smoke.

F. The stream of tocopherol that pours into the world economy has one of its main sources in us. To be looked to, likewise, as a fountainhead of tocopherol research suits us. The greater number of disinterested investigators we can incite to scrutinize the role and fate of tocopherol in mammalian and avian physiology, the prouder we shall be.

G. Until the fundamentals of chemistry had been discovered, metallurgy was purely an art; but, after it became possible to study the composition of metals and alloys and the chemical processes involved in extracting metals, the science of metallurgy began to take form. Today we speak of metallurgy as an art and a science, because, in spite of the great strides which have been taken by the physical sciences, metallurgy still contains some unexplained phenomena, still makes use of some rule-of-thumb methods, and still finds it necessary to employ artisans to do work which cannot be learned from scientific textbooks.

H. They were by no means untalkative; but thanks to the self-training in discretion their role demands, the initial picture was one of uniform well-adjustment—in most cases, it would seem, the husband was ambitious and she was proud for him, the company was terribly decent about everything, and the boss and his wife just couldn't have been nicer to Ed and me, etc. By the topics they involuntarily brought up, however, by the topics they avoided, and by their choice of words, they could generally produce a more rounded picture. For this reason, interviews were not of the question-and-answer type, but more in the nature of those termed "depth" and "unstructured," i.e., long and rambling.

I. Additional variations in cure time and pot life can be accomplished by varying the curing agent concentration up or down from 1%. For a given pot life the cure time can be shortened by increasing the temperature of the part to 150-200°F. during cure.

When necessary to extend the pot life, it has been found desirable to store the catalyzed compound at a reduced temperature such as 0°F.

J. Each groove on the stereo record has two sound tracks containing both lateral and vertical modulation. In order to pick up the two sound tracks, a stereophonic cartridge equipped with a small diameter stylus has been developed to move both laterally and vertically simultaneously. This stylus reproduces the lateral and vertical modulations contained in each groove wall and channels the information to the proper amplifier and speaker. The information contained on the inner groove wall is fed to the right hand speaker whereas the information on the outer groove wall is fed to the left hand speaker.

3. What audiences seem to have been intended for the following?

A. Flywell Aircraft Corporation's deliveries for 1958 increased 527 units over the previous year, a gain of 22%. The Company estimates that it did 49.98% of business plane sales among the leading small-plane manufacturers—Aeropush, Propoco, Flywell, and Hifly.

B. This year, for the first time, Flywell is forging ahead of rival Propoco Aircraft as the No. 1 maker of private planes. Flywell's performance is proof that the private-aircraft industry, which sprouted like a teen-ager after 1951, has finally matured. Last year, U.S. private-plane manufacturers delivered 6,416 planes, up 300 over 1957, raked in $101,500,000 v. $99,700,000 in 1957. In January, the latest month reported, they sold 100 more planes and grossed $2,500,000 more than in January, 1958. The recession proved that for the businessman, the private plane is not a luxury but a necessity.

C. It has been calculated that an airplane flying at sea level at 700 miles per hour would be heated 100 degrees just by air friction —100 degrees above the temperature the air already has. Add to this the heating effect of sunshine, the heat from the engines, and so forth, and you begin to realize that this plane would not only be too hot for comfort, but would actually be weakened.

D. Critical heat transfer problems occur in the continuum flow regime. The flow field around a wing leading edge exhibits a characteristic bow shock wave, or a layer of ionized hot gas between the shock and the surface, as well as a layer over the surface where the temperature of the gas drops sharply to its value at the surface. Heat energy becomes transferred to the airplane by conduction and diffusion from the boundary layer, and by radiation from hot gases in the shock layer, mostly in ultraviolet–near-infrared portions of the spectrum.

E. Though the molecules (or atoms) of a solid are quiet, compared with the molecules of a gas or even a liquid, they do move around some, like a horse tethered to a peg in a clover patch. The scientist says they "move around positions of equilibrium," which is fair enough.

F. As soon as a positive electron encounters a negative one, their electric charges will immediately cancel one another and the two electrons will cease to exist as individual particles. Such a process of mutual annihilation of two electrons results, however, in the birth of an intensive electromagnetic radiation (gamma rays) escaping from the point of the encounter and carrying with it the original energy of the two vanished particles.

POST-MORTEM ON THE PRACTICE PROBLEMS

1. This report is an example of *suggesting* rather than *telling* a message. Although it starts out objectively, it soon introduces an attempt at ironic understatement: "... it was realized that they mere taking surprising liberties with the laws of mechanics." The arrangement of authorities is also suggestive. The Director of NICAP is made to appear as though he were giving the sighting fullest benefit of doubt, but actually his comment is used to emphasize the doubt. The irony of the last sentence is more obvious. (This student-written report was intentionally slanted.)

2. The publications in which the excerpts originally appeared may indicate their intended function:

A. This excerpt originally appeared in "Tests for Tomorrow," *Boeing Magazine,* July, 1958, pp. 12-13. Its language is too "cute" (e.g., "It is built like an iceberg.") to be appropriate for a formal report, but is quite appropriate for a journal circulated among the general public, where the intent is only to sharpen interest.

B. Although this excerpt might very well have been part of a report recommending commercial development of the Tesla turbine, its original function was simply to explain some of the work accomplished by Nikola Tesla in an article entitled "Nikola Tesla —Last of the Pioneers?" by Leland J. Anderson in *Journal of Engineering Education,* XLIX (June, 1959), 969-970.

C. This "excerpt" is really a composite of similar paragraphs appearing in brochures descriptive of company facilities. Their function is usually to impress potential customers with the size and capability of equipment. The dramatic language is probably intended to impress them also with the idea that nobody loafs around here—not even the report writers.

D. This paragraph is from Jonathan Swift's classic *Gulliver's Travels,* Book III, Chap. 2. Its function is obviously to amuse, but in its context it also makes some telling points for good scientific method as opposed to abstract boondoggling.

E. This excerpt originally appeared in a report entitled "The ABC's of Thermonuclear Fusion Energy" by Hugh Taylor and Arthur V. Tobolsky in *American Scientist,* XLVI (Summer, 1958), 196. Its function was to acquaint the general scientific public (more specialized than the public who reads *Scientific American*) with some basic principles at a time when atomic fusion was coming into prominence as alternative to atomic fission as a source of power.

F. The function of this excerpt was obviously to sell a brand of tocopherol; the national advertising campaign during 1958 was limited, of course, to medical and scientific journals.

G. This typical textbook excerpt is from Joseph Newton's *An Introduction to Metallurgy* (2nd ed., New York: Wiley, 1947, p. 2), where it served to introduce students to the historical background of metallurgy.

H. This excerpt is from William H. Whyte, Jr., *Is Anybody Listening?* (New York: Simon and Schuster, 1952, pp. 148-149) and demonstrates how description of procedure is pleasantly introduced into a popular report of this kind. This description, in fact, appeared in a footnote where it might easily have been ignored.

I. This typical excerpt of a procedure specification issued with technical products is from General Electric's "Silicones Product Data," No. R-159, but note that it hedges a bit. The reason for the hedging is that the product was still in the research stage when the specification was issued. Most specifications do not hedge.

J. This paragraph is from the dust jacket of an RCA record, advertising stereophonic records by explaining how they work.

3. Again, the original publication in which the excerpts appeared may indicate the intended audience:

A. This typical paragraph is a composite of brief paragraphs appearing in such journals as *Iron Age, Business Week, Aviation Week,* and *Forbes Magazine,* usually accompanied by graphs or photographs. They are meant for a management-type skimming reader who wants to get an over-all view of a situation without bothering about details.

B. This composite paragraph is typical of articles which summarize financial reports in the weekly news magazines, such as *Newsweek, Time,* or *U.S. News and World Report,* whose readers represent a much broader range of interests than those of people who read the journals noted in (A). Note, incidentally, how the news magazines like to feed the public fancy for statistics, and also how they try to relate facts and figures to over-all trends (e.g., "The recession proved..."), another attractive feature for the busy reader who wants to be well informed in a hurry.

C. This excerpt is from Willy Ley, *Satellites, Rockets, and Outer Space* (New York: New American Library, 1958, p. 19). It is typical of reports on space technology which appeared in newspapers to satisfy the nation's sudden hunger for information following Sputnik. It is, of course, geared to the most general reader.

D. This composite excerpt, by contrast, is typical of reports on space technology which appeared about the same time for the broad scientific and engineering readers who had not been trained in aerodynamics or astronautics but realized that Sputnik marked the real beginning of the present technological revolution in the giant aircraft business.

E. This brief excerpt should be enough to identify its source as a popular book on a technical subject. Monroe Upton's *Electronics for Everyone* is a paperback (New York: New American Library, 1957) and good example of texts designed to teach anyone willing to learn. Since their audience is very broad, the subject must be enlivened with whatever the author's imagination can contrive.

F. This excerpt is also from a paperback on a technical subject: George Gamow, *One Two Three . . . Infinity* (New York: New American Library, 1953) . But it is obviously intended for a much more erudite audience than Upton's readers. In fact, this passage is one of the simplest ones in Gamow's book, but the book as a whole is enlivened with enough funny sketches and humorous stories to hold a wide audience.

CHAPTER 2

Planning

Considering the general requirements discussed in the previous chapter, a report writing project should begin with determining (1) what you are going to talk about, (2) why, and (3) to whom. The subject, purpose, and audience are your basic design requirements and will determine what weight of information you must convey, what the structure of the report must be, and what kind of details will be needed to support the structure. These requirements are best brought into focus by preparing a target statement and a program plan, which will serve as a statement of work to be performed and a schedule of performance.

1. IDENTIFY THE REAL SUBJECT

Start by asking about your *real* subject, because the first rule of any kind of writing is: know what you are talking about. It is not enough to know your subject. You must be sure of what you want to say about that subject. Suppose, for example, that you are an expert on world population problems and you want to write about what you know. It would take a book—maybe many volumes—to tell all you know. So you decide to concentrate on one aspect, the rising rate of increase in world population since 1945. This topic also would fill a book. Therefore you decide to limit yourself to three causes of increase: control of disease, reduction of infant mortality, and lengthening of life expectancy. Any one of these three would be a good topic for a report 100 to 150 pages long. But having now broken your subject down into workable parts you can choose from the alternatives. Your over-all subject is world population problems, but your *real* subject could be either control of disease, reduction of infant mortality, or extension of life expectancy.

The problem in choosing your real subject is keeping the topic broad enough so that it is worth reading about—yet not so broad that it cannot be handled within the limits of length you set for yourself. The inexperienced writer usually attempts to cover too much ground and uses a shotgun approach, hoping to hit a target by grace of the law of averages. The result is toroballistics.[1] Just as bad is the writer at the other extreme who limits his topic so narrowly that it could be covered on a post-card. In either case, the broad topic will not have the support it deserves, and the narrow topic will have to be padded with repetition, verbiage, and irrelevant digressions.

The solution to selecting a real and workable subject is to look at it graphically so that it may be seen in proper relation to other topics within its subject area. There are two ways of doing this. The first is to use concentric circles; the other is to use the familiar method of outlining.

Start, for example, with a big circle representing "Population Expansion since World War II" and within this circle draw a smaller circle representing the general heading "Causes of Rate of Increase." Then within that circle include smaller circles representing smaller topics—"control of disease," "decline of infant mortality," and "extension of life expectancy." And, of course, you could then include smaller circles within the last three. Under "control of disease," for example, you might represent public health measures such as mosquito control, water treatment, and antibiotic treatment. This process could continue until you have exhausted the possibilities under the general heading; then you would be in the best position to see a wise choice.

The process of outlining consists of preparing a random list

[1] Toroballistics—the ancient art of bull shooting.

of everything you can think of about the subject. Then you look over the list for overlapping or repeating items, and especially for similarities and differences that would enable you to form major and minor headings and subheadings in outline form, thus:

  I. Population expansion since World War II.
    A. Causes of the high rate of increase.
      1. Control of disease.
      2. Reduction of infant mortality.
      3. Expansion of life expectancy.

On the basis of this preliminary outline you can choose one of the topics for further exploration:

  I. Control of disease.
    A. Mosquito control.
    B. Water purification.
    C. Distribution of antibiotics.

Then it is a question of how much further the topic needs to be broken down.

Some people find it helpful to use different kinds of outlining schemes according to the nature of the ideas they are working with. For instance, an outline concerned with simple classification might look like this:

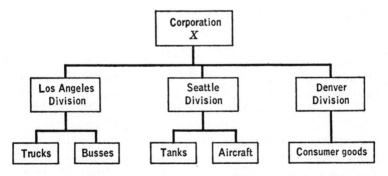

An outline concerned with the relationships of one part of a thing to other parts of the same thing might look like this:

DIVISION PROPOSALS GROUP

$$
\text{Proposals} \atop \text{Management}
\begin{cases}
\text{Systems Analysis} & \begin{cases} \text{Systems Proposals} \\ \text{Subsystems Proposals} \\ \text{Subcontract Proposals} \end{cases} \\
\\
\text{R\&D Programs} & \begin{cases} \text{Study Proposals} \\ \text{R\&D Proposals} \end{cases} \\
\\
\text{Marketing Relations} & \begin{cases} \text{Brochures} \\ \text{Presentation Aids} \\ \text{Marketing Support} \end{cases}
\end{cases}
$$

And an outline concerned with the sequence of events might take this standard form:

STEPS IN PROPOSAL MANAGEMENT

I. Study the proposal request.
   A. Does it fall within our product area?
   B. Are we committed to this type of work?
   C. What are the requirements?
   D. Can we devote full effort to it?
II. Establish a proposals plan.
   A. Outline criteria and assign best people to achieve them.
   B. Prepare an outline of responsibilities and functions.
   C. Establish schedules with firm milestones.
   D. Call a kick-off meeting with entire proposal team.

2. PINPOINT YOUR PURPOSE

Before you can establish the limits of your subject, you have to consider your reason for writing the report. You will find it helpful to distinguish between your *objective*—the long-range goal—and your *purpose*—the immediate step in achieving that goal. Thus you can think in these terms: "The *objective* of this report is to help solve problems created by rapidly expanding world population. The *purpose* is to analyze the high rate of increase since 1945." Or "The *objective* of this report is to explain the high rate of increase in world population since 1945. The *purpose* is to analyze the causes of the increase." Not only thinking this way, but actually writing down statements of objective and purpose will help you focus on your purpose and subject as well. You may find that you have primary objectives and secondary objectives, but you ought to end up with only one purpose. And if you have trouble finding them, you can use the methods you used in focusing on a subject—going around in geometric circles or outlining.

Pinpointing the purpose of a report is relatively easy. Since reports are intended to be useful, your statement of purpose would naturally include some concept of how your information would be used. If your field is engineering, for example, your information might be useful in an area such as, determining design or system requirements, developing a product, providing a service, analyzing or testing a model, or reducing costs. If your field is business, your report might be useful in planning, organizing, directing, or controlling the areas of manpower, money, materials, manufacturing, marketing, or management. Reports in any field perform useful functions that can be summarized as follows:

Analyze problem areas, as in a high-level discussion of genetics or inertial guidance or business cycles.

Describe a situation, as in a survey of developments in protein synthesis, or prestressed concrete, or computer applications for small business.

Explain techniques, as in a report on sterilizing with radiation, or the operation of numerically controlled machines, or the automation of supermarket checkout counters.

Report achievement, as in progress reports, routine activity reports, or final reports documenting experiments, test programs, trips, or operations.

The function of a report will often determine the form of the report, as Table I will show.

3. AIM AT AN AUDIENCE

The purpose of a report will be partly determined by who will read and use it. You will want to know not only how he will use it, but how much he already knows about the subject

TABLE I. Common Types of Report

Function	Type	Description
1. Quick, specific information — frequently informal, "one-shot" messages not meant to be matters of record.	Printed "action memo" form or printed memo sheets with spaces for filling in blanks.	These prepared forms sometimes require only a checkmark in an appropriate square to indicate their message. Sometimes longer ones require filling in blanks or answering specific questions. Short ones are usually handwritten; longer ones are typed for courtesy.
2. Information about policy or in reply to questions or reporting status briefly — informal but for the record.	Correspondence: in memorandum form (for interdepartment) or in letters (for outside the company).	Informal correspondence of this type is best kept to one topic, and should follow the pattern described on page 68: Point-Discussion-Action or Examples. Typed, of course.
3. Information for record, reference, long-term use. Seldom more than six pages long.	Letter report (report in form of letter) or memorandum report, according to destination.	These are reports in every respect except that the subject heading substitutes for a title page. They should make use of headings and subheadings when appropriate; should state authorization, purpose, and scope; and should summarize, as in longer reports. They are more formal than standard correspondence, and are carefully typed.
4. Administrative or summary information offering comprehensive view of an over-all situation in compressed form — usually without much detail.	Formal, summary report, such as a Monthly Operations Report, or Annual Activities Report.	These summarize highlights and only typical or sample facts and figures. They are usually semitechnical and aimed at a broad nonspecialist audience. Sometimes they are elaborately printed. Often they are illustrated, and they may have many tables and appendixes.

5. Information for publication in a journal, reporting achievement or discussing a problem.	Article for technical journal.	Features "deck" or summarizing sentence which is an abstract of the article; followed by introduction, discussion, and summarizing concluding sentence or paragraph. Headings and subheads are in order; so are summarizing tables and illustrations. Should be journal-oriented — that is, patterned after other articles appearing in the destined journal.
6. Information to support a bid or proposal.	Formal proposal.	These are usually prepared to specifications given in a request for proposal or established by company policy. Most common format is: foreword, summarizing introduction, description of management plan, discussion of technical plan, description of capability. These are, of course, customer-oriented and carefully prepared to convince him of your capability to do the proposed task better than anyone else in the business.
7. Information about a complete program of work, for reference and permanent record.	Technical report.	These are fully described in Chapter 3. They differ from shorter, more informal reports and articles in containing full details about the program. They are usually submitted in typescript for subsequent reprinting.
8. Information about a product or process, telling how to use it or how to do it.	Manual.	May appear in a variety of formats (manuals, handbooks, "specifications," etc.) but always follow a logical, step-by-step arrangement, e.g., what to do — how to do; what is it — how is it used — how is it kept in repair, etc.
9. Information covering all that is known about a subject within specified limits.	Monograph.	Thorough, textbook treatment requires full illustration and documentation.

and what else he needs to know. These factors will determine the type of information you must find and the form of presentation—specific or general, complex or simple, technical or nontechnical. But here again the problem is relatively easy to solve.

Most reports are generally written for a management audience, whether top management or staff management. Top management makes decisions on planning, organizing, directing, and controlling operations. Staff management makes recommendations affecting top management's decisions and is concerned with "problem-solving" rather than "decision-making." Specialists on subordinate levels will usually supply staff management with the facts and figures upon which decisions are eventually based.

Because of this separation of interests, most reports consist of three levels of information—going from the general, simple, and nontechnical (for top management skimming) to the specific, complex, and technical (for study by the specialists). It is as though the reports were saying:

To top management—"Here is the over-all situation."
To staff management—"Here are the chief facts and figures."
To specialists—"Here are all the facts and figures."

We will see later how these three levels of information are handled in the report itself. In the planning stage, it is necessary to keep in mind that you will need to serve the three types of readers unless you already know that you are going to serve only one type. Most writers will sensibly assume that they are writing for specialists and will collect all the information they can. But if you know now that you will aim only at staff or at top management, do not waste your time looking for specialized details that will not be relevant to your purpose.

4. PREPARE A TARGET STATEMENT

To make sure that you have focused on your subject, purpose, and audience it is a good idea to prepare a target statement or preliminary topic sentence. This statement should summarize (1) what you are talking about, (2) why you are talking about it, and (3) whom you are talking to. It could be printed on a card tacked above your desk and provide a target to shoot at while you plan, organize, compose, and revise your report.

You can compose your target statement by simplifying your real subject to a key word or two. Think about these key words as a title that tells what your report should contain. Try to make it show exactly what you hope to say; imagine how it will look indexed along with many other titles concerned with the same subject. Will it distinguish your report from others? Will it tell the reader exactly what your report is about?

EXAMPLES	COMMENT
Not: Flaws	1. Too broad.
But: Mechanical Flaws in Low-Alloy 7604 Steel	2. It should name the contents of the report, and not more than the report contains.
Not: Mechanical Flaws in Low-Allow 7604 Steel Used for Nonstructural Applications	3. Too detailed and too long.
But: Mechanical Flaws in Low-Alloy Steels: Nonstructural	4. It should be brief enough to be read at a glance, without sacrificing clearness for brevity. A subtitle should be used when the subject is complex, detailed, or limited.
Not: Final Report of a Program to Evaluate the Necessity of Establishing a Correlation between Mechanical Flaws and Reject Rates	5. Wordy, imprecise.
But: Correlation of Mechanical Flaws and Rejects in Low-Alloy Steels: Final Report	6. It should omit superfluous words, like "Study of," "Investigation of," but may use a by-line for this kind of information.

Use the title as the *subject* of your target statement. The *predicate* of the sentence will be what you are going to say about the subject. Thus you can formulate your target statement in these steps:

1. Determine the REAL SUBJECT.
   a. This department runs tests on brazing methods using electric conduction heat.

   This answers *what the department does.*

   b. Tests on brazing methods using electric conduction heat are run in this department.

   This answers *what the work is.*

   c. Tests in this department are on brazing methods using electric conduction heat.

   This answers *what the tests are.*

   d. Brazing methods using electric conduction heat are tested in this department.

   This answers *what is tested.*

2. Set the LIMITS OF THE SUBJECT.
   a. Steel balls had disadvantages.
   b. Steel balls had three disadvantages.
   c. Difficult welding, instability, and fracturing made steel balls unusable.

   Note how focusing on the real subject points out the generality of the subject in the first two versions.

3. Set the LIMITS OF THE PREDICATE.
   a. The tips were drilled.
   b. The tips were drilled to accommodate smaller steel balls.
   c. The tips were drilled to accommodate the ³⁄₁₆-inch diameter steel balls.

   Note how the predicate is limited by specific words.

Imagine your target statement as the *message* you will want to leave in your reader's mind when he has finished reading the report. Then simplify your purpose to a word or two, and imagine it as the *impression* you would like your reader to carry away from your report:

"We had better do this or else . . ."
"We might try that . . ."
"Here's how we can do this . . ."
"So these are the facts . . ."
"Yes, this problem needs further study . . ."

And, finally, write down the name of your intended audience. The three elements can then be combined into one sentence. You may find it helpful to put your target statement into the form of a question:

"Should Congress be persuaded that free distribution of antibiotics will increase the rate of population increase?"
or
"Should the World Health Organization be advised that water treatment is the only feasible way of checking dysentery?"
or
"Should we recommend that the Government of Malaya initiate spraying DDT for mosquito control?"
or
"Should Mr. Brady be warned to purchase a new fan for the drying room?"

Concentrate on answering your target question and this will give your work the focus necessary to enable planning with a purpose.

5. PLAN A PROGRAM

A well-planned program of experimental or test work will go far toward ensuring a good report. If you look at the entire program as a closed-end system—planning at the beginning, report at the end—whatever happens in between will have a certain focus, or at least a beginning and an end. To see how program planning is reflected in report preparation, consider the following outline:

PROGRAM PLANNING

I. What is the problem?
II. Is resolving it justified? What are the effects in terms of costs, production, efficiency, etc.? What are the causes? Is the situation local or general?

REPORT PREPARATION

Questions I and II will be treated in your introduction and are basic to your target statement.

III. What is the best way to solve it?
What basic assumptions apply?
What will we need to do the job?
What data do we want?
What quantity of specimens for reliable results?
What results can be anticipated?
When can we do it?
How much will it cost?

These details will form the nucleus and bulk of the report. Clear, careful notes taken while the planning and work progresses can often be absorbed into the text with only minor revision.

One type of program planning that lends itself readily to absorption into a report is shown on p. 37.

You will find that this planning form lends itself easily to the industrial formats described later. The title could be carried over intact. The paragraph headed "Problem" is easily expanded into an introduction. The "Approach" provides a summary of experimental procedure. At this point, you need add only results, analysis, and conclusion.

Although designed chiefly for industrial testing, the method suggested by this form is also adaptable to other fields with appropriate modifications. Its advantages offset whatever pain is involved in preparing it. It offers an extended target statement, plus a breakdown of planned procedure. It also offers an estimate of time and costs, plus ready adaptability to report preparation.

Here is how the same method may be used in planning a report writing program:

TARGET STATEMENT: What should the Director know about current methods of correcting ballistic trajectories of space vehicles in free flight?

PROGRAM: It is proposed to investigate developments pertinent to the following problem areas:
1. Braking impulse required to start a space vehicle on a controlled descent trajectory from a circular orbit.
2. Correction of elliptical orbits in the solar system.
3. Terminal attraction of the targets' gravitational field.

PROGRAM: Evaluating Radio Hook-Up Wire Insulations
at Temperatures from 100° to 500° F.

PROBLEM: The objective of this program is to evaluate ability of
five types of radio hook-up wire insulation to withstand temperatures from 100° to 500° F. This evaluation is necessary because most rework and replacements on rejected radio products
have been attributed to wire insulation failure at these temperatures. Results of this program should provide designers with
reliable data.

APPROACH: Samples of each of five high-temperature wire insul-
ations will be tested over the temperature range (100°-500° F.) in
a small electric oven. Some will be heated continuously to failure.
Others will be exposed to successively higher temperatures but
will be returned to room temperature periodically. Types to be
tested include:
Hefty, type A (extruded)
Hefty, type 20-A (extruded)
Spun Hefty Fiber Braid
Rubber Glass Braid
Each type will be heated in seven configurations and two different
test sequences. The wire will be tested wound around a spool in
tension; wound around a square spool; and in cable form.

SCHEDULE:

Phase	Start	Complete	Description
I	11/25/60	12/25/60	Design oven control fixtures and request fabrication.
II	12/25/60	1/8/61	Set up test equipment and prepare samples, test sequence, and data sheets.
III	1/8/61	2/20/61	Run tests.
IV	2/20/61	3/20/61	Prepare and publish report.

ESTIMATED HOURS: Engineering Hours—400
Shop Hours—150

ESTIMATED MATERIALS COST: $500.00

Prepared by: Ralph Hearne   Date: 11/1/61

PROBLEM: Midcourse corrections can range from single velocity impulses to continuous thrusting programs. Midcourse corrections are often suggested as a solution to ballistic errors, but very little fundamental scientific engineering on the subject has been publicized.

APPROACH: Preliminary research will consist of surveying published literature to determine basic mathematical theory of existing guidance systems. This will be followed by a program of interviews and correspondence with industrial firms and government agencies concerned with space technology. The results of the survey will then be analyzed and mathematically checked out.

SCHEDULE:

PHASE	START	COMPLETE	DESCRIPTION
I	11/25/60	12/25/60	Preliminary survey of published literature.
II	12/25/60	1/8/61	Compilation of basic mathematical calculations.
III	1/8/61	2/20/61	Interviews at JPL, NAA, Hughes, STL, Aerospace. Correspondence with AIA, NASA, ARPA, and USAF.
IV	2/20/61	3/20/61	Analysis and interpretation of data—preparation of report.

ESTIMATED HOURS: 500
ESTIMATED COST (postage, transportation): $35.00

A plan for organizing and composing the report may consist of a preliminary checklist something like the following:

1. Collect information.
2. Choose an appropriate report form.
3. Prepare outline with main and subordinate headings.
4. Write the rough draft—introduction, discussion, conclusion.
5. Prepare a table of contents and summary as a check on arrangement, consistency, and relevance.
6. Prepare supplements such as appendixes, bibliography, and letter of transmittal.
7. Review and revise the rough draft.
8. Prepare final copy.
9. Proofread.
10. Submit.

Target dates for each step will add challenge to the job and give your activities a practical framework. Moreover, you can keep track of how much you have accomplished and how much more remains to be done. A chart showing flow time, milestones (target dates for specific tasks), and completion dates can serve this purpose easily, as shown in Figure 1.

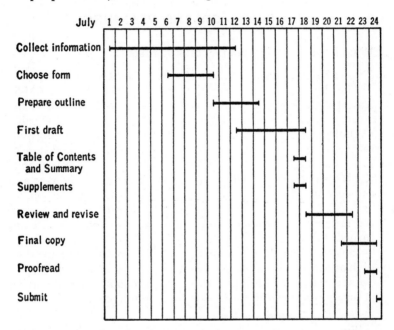

Figure 1. Sample Planning Form for Scheduling Report-Writing Activities.

The advantage of program planning is that it gives you a structured outline of what you are going to do, why you are going to do it, how you are going to do it—and where you hope to end. The major steps should be clearly marked and some of the subsidiary steps as well. Thus you can avoid that hollow feeling which comes from wondering "What will I do now?" And, more important, you can see the relevance and importance of every step you take. This will give your work purpose and direction, and will result in the professional quality of preconceived design, discussed in the introduction. From a practical point of view, the time devoted to planning is well worth the time saved in subsequent phases of designing and constructing the report. This saving will be immediately reflected as soon as you begin to compile the information you need.

PRACTICE PROBLEMS: PLANNING

1. What is the real subject of the following report?

Transducer Calibration Assures Accurate Test Data

The first squadron for operational use of the Bell GAM-63 Rascal air-to-surface guided missile was actitvated recently by the Strategic Air Command. Launchings of Rascal are now being made from B-47 bombers flown by SAC crews for training purposes and to permit the squadron to reach an operational state as soon as possible. Rascal, which is 32 feet long and 4 feet in diameter, is designed to be carried aloft by bombers such as the B-47 and can be released miles from the target without exposing the bomber and its crew to enemy defenses. The missile actually flies toward the target at supersonic speed while the launching aircraft has turned and is enroute to its base.

In recent tests, the air-to-surface Rascal roared through the skies high over New Mexico to score four direct hits, demonstrating pinpoint accuracy. Behind this success story is another story involving accuracy and reliability—the reliability of test data.

Calibrating Transducer Data

Throughout the development of the Rascal "pilotless bomber," Bell rocket test cells operated day and night testing rocket motors and components for Rascal and other projects. CEC Type 4-311 and 4-312 Pressure Pickups, with the Type 5-119 Recording Oscillograph, played important roles in sensing and recording data.

Electrically, the CEC transducer is a four-arm bridge composed of unbonded strain gages. The instrument has excellent frequency response, reliability, and accuracy, but its optimum performance depends on auxiliary equipment and techniques. To improve the accuracy of test data, the Bell Aircraft engineering laboratories adopted a special calibration system for strain-gage transducers.

About five years ago, Bell Aircraft personnel used a four-wire voltage method for calibration of resistance strain-gage pressure transducers. A shunt resistor across one leg of the bridge in the transducer determined network sensitivity. Because the voltage method introduced errors of 2–4%, Bell instrumentation engineers turned to an error-eliminating current calibration system.

Leads Reduce Accuracy

The instrumentation system at the test cells is a large complex network, consisting of cables and patch boards connecting the instruments to central recording and control areas. These conditions result in long leads from transducer to recording instrument—leads which appear as resistances in series with the strain gage bridge and measuring instrument circuit. These lead resistances have decreased accuracy by the 2–4% figure; a condition caused by the four-wire voltage calibration method. . . .

A six-wire voltage calibration system would have eliminated the lead resistance error. However, the cost of system modification and test cell time eliminated this possibility. Safety regulations prevented installation and operation of the calibration equipment at the transducer locations. A third solution was selection of the current calibration system.

CEC Recordings, March-April, 1958, p. 13.

2. Listed below are thirty-six titles selected at random from student reports. To assist you in evaluating them, here is a check list of areas a title might cover: can you tell what the report is about?

Product Area	1. Product?
	2. Service?
	3. Capability?
Problem Area	4. Methods?
	5. Materials?
	6. Machines?
Project Area	7. Survey?
	8. Investigation?
	9. Operation?

Titles
1. Vertical-Takeoff Aircraft
2. An Introduction to the MASER
3. Inertial Effects in a Multi-Ball Transmission
4. Desmodronic Valves for Internal Combustion Engines
5. Application of Light Sensing Devices to Space Vehicle Attitude Control

6. Escape Capsules for High Performance Aircraft
7. Design and Principles of Air-Cushion Craft
8. Application of the Tunnel Diode
9. Taped Machining Control in the Automotive Industry
10. General Requirements for Flight Equipment Static Power Converters in Ranger 3
11. Photogrammetry as a Method of Photographic Mapping
12. "Rex Slip-Form Paver" as Replacement for Header Paving Equipment
13. Individual Air-Conditioning Systems for Industrial and Farm Use
14. Industrial Applications of Epoxy Resins
15. Improvement of Rise Time in Transistorized Astable Multi-vibrators Through Use of Semiconductor Diodes
16. NSU-Wankel Internal Combustion Engine
17. Developments in Microwave Communication, 1960-1965
18. Improvement of Potentiometric Output in Pressure Transducers
19. Electronic Data Processing in Industry
20. Microminiaturization
21. Passive Infrared Countermeasures for Aircraft Against Missiles
22. Prestressed Concrete Beams in Bridges and Buildings
23. Computer Applications in Small Business
24. Development of Traffic Control Devices in Los Angeles County
25. Electronic Aids in Commercial Photography Studios
26. Comparative Evaluation of Digital and Analogue Computers
27. Boundary Layer Control: Effects on Sailplane Performance
28. Experimental Determination of Several Properties of Light
29. Plastic Welding
30. Thermoelectricity
31. Passive Defense System Against Infrared Missile Attack
32. Developments in Surveyor's Transits
33. Trends in Home Television
34. Program for Improving Reliability of Inertial Navigation Gyroscopes
35. Slip-Form Paving Reduces Highway Construction Cost
36. Digital Computers as Design Tools for the Electronic Engineer

3. Here are five different versions of the same information. Determine the level of the intended audience in each case.

   A. *Cryoforming,* named after cryogenics—the scientific field concerned with behavior of materials at low temperatures down to

—459.6°F.—uses a known metallurgical transformation occurring in a metal during heat-treatment. A machined, formed, or welded part is heated to 1725°F. as part of the hardening process. Then it is cooled to slightly above 200°F. and forced into a sizing die (also at 200°F.), where it is clamped or held by the pressure of the die. Both part and die are then cooled gradually to −110°F. in a solution of dry ice and trichloroethylene, or in a dry cold box. During this cooling cycle, the transformation takes place—the crystalline structure of the metal changes. In stainless steels for example molecules of carbon and iron realign to form new structures. There are no residual stresses and thus no warping, wrinkling, or bowing. Springback is eliminated. CRC has held a tolerance of 0.002 for each 12 inches of a 36-inch part (the thickness of a human hair) made of PH 17-7 stainless steel.

B.   COMMUNICATION RESEARCH CENTER
State College Drive
Los Angeles 32

10 December 19—

Mr. James Rogers, Chief
Tool and Die Department
Loughnutt Aircraft Corp.
East Lynn Boulevard
Pageboy, Ohio

Dear Sir:

Your 6 December letter requested information concerning close-tolerance forming of stainless steels. A tolerance nearly ten times greater than required by your firm has been achieved using cryoforming methods with PH 17-7 stainless steel. Cryoforming employs the principle of polymorphic transformation at low temperatures, to remove residual stresses accumulated during fabrication.

The procedure of cryoforming begins with heating the fabricated part at 1725°F. and cooling it to slightly above 200°F. It is then forced into a sizing die (also at 200°F.), and secured in place. The part and die are cooled slowly to −110°F. in a dry cold box or a heat transfer solution. During the cooling process recrystallization within the part begins at the inversion temperature. Recrystallization causes reorientation of the crystal fabric which dissipates residual stresses generated prior to recrystallization. A tolerance of 0.002 inches for each 12 inches of a 36-inch part has been realized using this method and the type of stainless steel previously mentioned.

Unfortunately no other quantitative results are available. Further experimentation is being conducted with many types of stainless steels and many treatment processes. When new developments become available, this firm will supply information on them on request.

Very truly yours,

Alexander Watt
Director of Research

C. Cryoforming has become part of the heat-treat process, which is carried out as follows: the machined, formed, or welded part is heated to 1725°F. in a furnace as part of the hardening process. This may result in warping or other distortion. The part, cooled to slightly above 200°F., is forced into a sizing die prewarmed to 200°F., and held by clamping, banding-and-wedging, or simply by the pressure of the die itself. Part and die are then cooled gradually. Final cooling, to as low as −110°F., is done in a solution of dry ice and trichloroethylene, or in a dry cold box.

At some stage during the cooling cycle a metallurgical transformation takes place, the crystalline structure of the metal changes; molecules of carbon and iron realign themselves to form new and permanent alliances.

During this transition the metal is believed to be momentarily pliable. The steel reforms in the precise dimensions to which it is being held at the time.

When parts are removed from the cryoforming dies, the tendency to warp or spring back no longer exists. Parts show a close fit to design dimensions and usually can be furnace-aged without further restraint. Wrinkling and bowed-out areas are erased. In one example, welded and machined T-shaped external attachment members for brazed panels were held to plus or minus .002 for each 12 inches of a 36-inch member. This tolerance is about the thickness of a human hair.

D.   COMMUNICATION RESEARCH CENTER
State College Drive
Los Angeles 32, California

13 December 19—

Loughnutt Aircraft Corp.
East Lynn Boulevard
Pageboy, Ohio

Attention: Mr. James Rogers, Chief
          Tool and Die Department
Gentlemen:

The following solution is offered to the problem which has been submitted concerning the forming to close tolerances of precision aircraft parts made from the precipitation hardening stainless steels.

The procedure which has been followed in the heat treatment of the machined parts has required a subsequent sizing process which has been proven unnecessary if the heat treatment procedure known as cryoforming is followed. The cryoforming process is accomplished in the following manner:

1. Heat the machined, formed, or welded part to 1725°F.
2. Cool to slightly above 200°F., and force into a sizing die which has been preheated to the same temperature.
3. Clamp the die securely, and cool both part and die gradually to −110°F. in a solution of dry ice and trichloroethylene, or in a dry cold box.

The use of the cryoforming process eliminates residual stresses, warping, wrinkling, bowing, and springback. Communication Research Center has held a tolerance of 0.002 for each 12 inches of a 36 inch part made of 17-7 stainless steel. This is well within the tolerance limits required by Loughnutt Aircraft Corp.

Very truly yours,

Alexander Watt
Director of Research

E.   COMMUNICATION RESEARCH CENTER
                State College Drive
             Los Angeles 32, California
                                      15 December 19—
Loughnutt Aircraft Corp.
East Lynn Boulevard
Pageboy, Ohio

Attention: Mr. James Rogers, Chief
          Tool and Die Department

Dear Sir:

In your letter of 6 December 1960 you asked about close-tolerance forming of stainless steels. We have been able to hold a tolerance of 0.002 for each 12 inches of a 36 inch part made of PH 17-7 stainless steel using the "Cryoforming" process.

In the "Cryoforming" process the machined, formed, or welded part is heated to 1725°F. as part of the hardening process. Then it is cooled to slightly over 200°F. and forced into a sizing die which is also at 200°F. where it is clamped or held by the pressure of the die. Both part and die are then cooled gradually to −110°F. in a dry cold box, or in a solution of dry ice and trichloroethylene. During this cooling cycle there is a transformation of the crystalline structure which eliminates residual stresses; thus there is no warping, wrinkling or bowing.

We made some experimental runs of the "Cryoforming" process with Ph 17-7 stainless steel and were able to hold a tolerance of 0.002 for each 12 inches of a 36-inch part. From the experimental runs it appears that "Cryoforming" will be less expensive than hot sizing. If you should make production runs with the "Cryoforming" process we would be interested in the costs and any problems that may develop in production run operations.

Very truly yours,

Alexander Watt
Director of Research
COMMUNICATION RESEARCH CENTER

4. Determine the purpose of each of the following discussions.

A. Heat transfer can take place in only three ways: convection currents, conduction, and radiation. Radiation becomes increasingly important to scientists because, at high temperatures or in a vacuum, it is the predominant or possibly the sole form of heat transfer. An understanding of radiation is particularly important today as man looks ahead to space travel. In space the vacuum exists, and high intensity heat radiation will be encountered.

In discussing heat transfer by radiation, clear terminology is important. Reflectance refers to that fraction of incident radiation that is reflected. The remaining fraction not reflected is absorbed when it strikes an opaque body. When given a numerical value it is called absorptance, and if the surface is at the same temperature as the radiator, absorptance is exactly equal to emittance. Emittance is the amount of energy emitted by a body related to the energy emitted by a perfect emitter given a value of unity. Thus, if reflectance (*p*) equals *x*, then absorptance (*a*) equals $1 - x$. And under conditions of temperature equilibrium, emittance (*e*) also equals $1 - x$.

In transferring heat through radiation, the reflectance and emittance of surfaces determine the amount of heat transferred, and the understanding of emittance becomes the key to the heat transfer problems occurring in space.

B. Plastic housings in all manner of sizes and shapes, used in an across-the-board list of products, are among the first big developments of the 1960's . . . an exciting clue to things ahead. Materials such as polypropylene are fast changing the face and function of many a product, lending new color and styling appeal, improved performance, and above all—*lower cost!*

Measured by yesterday's standards the achievements of today's new materials border on the impossible: they provide high resistance to heat, moisture, household chemicals, foods, and cosmetics. They offer rich color and are ideally adaptable to the attractive styling requirements of modern merchandising. Yet because they are low-cost materials, adaptable to rapid cycling injection-molding, they are *priced right!*

No wonder that just about every new plastic housing project you see these days is a polypropylene project.

C. Some day the stellar equivalent of an archeologist will ferret his way through space, collecting debris from the sundry objects we are thrusting out past the pale of gravitation. That man is going to find a lot of glass. Next to the metals, glass is *the* basic material for space work. Big claim? Big fact.

You can blast glass out at the stars, shine the sun at it full open, slide it into the cold void of the earth's shadow, plummet it back to earth's searing atmosphere, recover it from the bobbing waves. And, all the time, glass will hold to its integrity, its properties, its dimensions.

You can design glass *into* a piece of space hardware; you can only know the beauty of this if you have had to design around some other material that has interesting properties but is hard to work. Glass has hardly any design limitations. You can mold it, blow it, fuse it, press and roll it, etch it, temper it, or try any of a dozen other controlled techniques to meet exactly the shape you want, exactly the exactness you want.

5. Draw up preliminary plans for a report on the subject described

in the following paragraph. (a) Prepare a target statement; (b) prepare a program plan; and (c) prepare a report plan.

Factors necessary for life are water, oxygen, suitable temperature, and favorable atmosphere. Nobody knows if Mars has water or water vapor in its atmosphere. If there is any oxygen, it is in negligible amounts. The temperatures are low and the atmosphere is too thin to protect life from radiation or sharp changes in temperatures. Yet color changes from brown to green in the "seas" of Mars suggest that there is some kind of life there. Possibly there are microorganisms which do not require oxygen and which can withstand extremes of temperature and bombardment of ultraviolet rays. If there are organisms, this suggests that the moisture environment is higher than previously suspected. If the color changes are not due to organisms, they may be due to some kind of mineral fluorescence or a refraction of light.

CHAPTER 3

Collecting Information

If you have planned well you should have a good notion of the kind and amount of information you will need. You will know whether to look for complex, technical, specific facts and figures, or simple, nontechnical, general information. You will also have some idea of what the finished report will contain and can thus estimate how much material to collect. As a rule of thumb, you will need supporting material (evidence, illustrations, etc.) in the proportion of four parts to one "structural" or major idea. But it is always a good plan to collect more information than you think you can use, for this will give you more flexibility to move around as you design and compose the report.

For most reports, information will consist of (1) facts and figures recorded during tests and investigations; (2) notes taken on books and journals; (3) response to direct inquiries by interview, questionnaire, and correspondence. Some helpful tips for compiling this information are outlined in this chapter.

1. RECORDING DATA

The check sheet shown below is typical of the kind used for recording engineering test data. It is easily adapted to tests in other fields wherever the circumstances surrounding the tests are important. Checking off each step requires you to take *all* significant data while the test is going on, or as soon as possible thereafter.

TYPICAL DATA SHEET

1. *Title.* An accurate, specific description of what you plan to do.
2. *Objective.* A simple straightforward answer to these questions:
   a. Why is the test being run?
   b. How is it being run?
   c. What is to be accomplished by running it this way?
3. *Test material.* Describe the type of material: form, condition, dimensions, nomenclature, and anything else that will serve for *exact* identification.
4. *Equipment.* List the type of equipment being used, with the manufacturer, size, and location. Also list any additional fixtures and any special equipment (do not bother to list manufacturer or model number of special equipment). Do not list such common items as 6-inch scales or common hand tools.
5. *General instructions.* Indicate preliminary operations performed before actual test and also operations performed periodically during the test, such as checking of machine settings. Keeping these general operations separate will avoid cluttering up "Test Procedure," which should concentrate on the actual conduct of the test.
6. *Test factors.* List *all* factors which may affect test results and explain how they are being handled, e.g., how are they being controlled? Specify also what results are being measured and how they are being measured.
7. *Test procedure.* Keep a running diary of what is done, step-by-step. Include appropriate sketches and tables. Tell what is being observed and how it is being recorded—including (when appropriate) samples of data sheets and curve sheets used for plotting data as the tests are being run.
8. *Results.* List *all* data, whether positive or negative, success or failure. Use tables and curves whenever appropriate, with descriptive captions and references to the run or phase of the test. This is "raw" data—you can polish it later, with neatly typed tables or carefully drawn diagrams.
9. *Analysis.* Explain how the data are analyzed: What assumptions are applied? What calculations are made? Sample calculations are very handy notes showing how data were analyzed.
10. *Conclusion.* What is your evaluation of the data? What conclusions can be drawn from the test? How do these conclusions relate to conclusions from other tests? And how do they relate to tests still to be made?

a. Tables

Tabulate whenever you have four or more sets of data. Tables are placed in an appendix when they contain a mass of numerical information requiring detailed analysis. Ordinarily, these tables are summarized in simpler tables integrated into the discussion. If the integrated tables are also long, they can sometimes be broken up into shorter units or summarized as summary tables.

Keep tables relevant. Tables support graphs or give information from them. They make comparisons easy for the reader, but should never be used for mere ornament. All tables must have bearing on the text and should be referred to in the discussion. Frequently, reference to the text is also carried in the caption of a table.

Title all tables. Tables are ordinarily titled and numbered at the top (other illustrations are usually titled below the figure). The title should be descriptive enough so that the table could stand independently if detached from the report. Every column in the table should be descriptively headed as well. Units in which the data is tabulated must be specified, and standard abbreviations or symbols should be used. Table II is an example of what a table looks like.

TABLE II. Comparative Cutting Speeds

Material	Max. Cutting Speed fpm		Remarks
	Rough Machined	Finish Machined	
Cast iron	50	60	Common gray-iron
Steel:			
Mild	70-75	85-90	No alloys, 0.15 to 0.20% carbon
High-carbon[a]	60	65	0.50% carbon, 1.15% manganese, 0.55% chromium
Tool	60	70	0.9 to 1% carbon, 25% manganese
Brass	100	100	
Aluminum	200	200	

[a] For hard steel, heat-treated and normalized, see Table XV, p. 8.

b. Graphs or Curves

Line graphs or curves are used when the rate of change of one
or two factors is of interest. They also point out an optimum
condition and the conditions accompanying it. Changes or trends
are indicated by changes in direction of the lines or curves connecting data points.

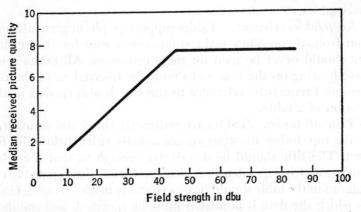

**Figure 2. Sample Graph. Idealized picture quality—field strength
characteristic. (Braum Hughes, "Studies of Picture Quality and Field
Strength," Proceedings of the IRE, June, 1960, p. 1057.)**

c. Charts

Careful selection of suitable scales is important. Generally,
the independent variable is used as the abscissa and the dependent variable as the ordinate. Except in unusual cases, only one
variable is used on the abscissa. Usually it is not good practice
to use exaggerated or suppressed-zero scales, but an exaggerated
scale can sometimes be used to advantage—for instance, when
the purpose is to show variation rather than general trends.

All scales should be labeled along the axes, indicating the units
plotted and their quantities, and should, of course, be drawn
clearly and legibly. (See Figure 2.)

Classified according to function, there are four types of charts:
engineering, operational, reference, and statistical. But for re-

port purposes they are usually classified as (1) picture charts or sketches, (2) line or bar charts, and (3) flow charts.

1. Picture charts or sketches are commonly used for nontechnical presentation of general information, familiar in newspaper articles where men in top hats are symbols of wealth, men in overalls symbols of labor, and so forth. In a report they should be treated like any other illustration and bear descriptive captions directly pertinent to the discussion.

2. Line or bar charts may be drawn vertically or horizontally to show by their length the frequency of data for a given point or set of points. Bar charts are useful for giving large volumes of data or for showing comparisons as for dates in scheduling. Pie charts, or circles in which the entire area represents 100 percent, are useful for giving percentage data.

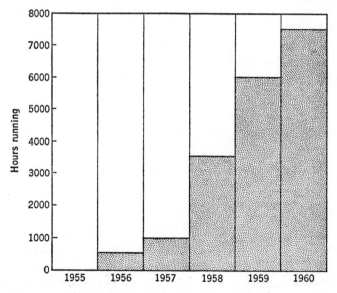

Figure 3. Sample Chart. The test program began in February, 1956, and is still running continuously after 7800 hours.

3. Flow charts diagram the actual, anticipated, or desired movement of supplies, personnel, documents, or equipment.

The common organizational chart is a type of flow chart, showing how lines of responsibility establish the flow of decisions and directives.

Some guide lines in the use of charts are as follows:

A good chart makes its point in 30 seconds or less. It is *informative, simple, direct.* It focuses on its message and hits only points of real significance. Its message is reduced to a simple sentence which is used as a caption to *tell* what the chart *shows.*

A good chart must be easy to understand. It tells its story in as few lines and words as possible. It discards everything except what is essential to its message, and uses only scales and figures necessary to clarify its point.

A good chart is easy to read. It gives a true picture by emphasizing proper relationships. Relationships are stressed rather than specific figures. Rounded figures or approximations are commonly used to facilitate comprehension and easy reading. Charts also make use of artwork to emphasize highlights and keep the eye moving from left to right rather than from lines to legend or caption, and then back to lines. In general, what a good chart tries to do is *summarize, simplify,* and *emphasize.* (See Figure 3.)

2. LIBRARY RESEARCH

a. Library Aids

A large part of prestudy before writing a report is often devoted to library research. For help in finding books and articles on your subject, there are many tools in the reference room of any library. The most generally helpful are listed below.

Readers' Guide to Periodical Literature. Index of general circulation magazines.
International Index to Periodicals. Index of "scholarly and highly specialized periodicals."
The New York Times Index. General index to news for specific years.
Technical Book Review Index. Index and digest of reviews and criticism of technical books.

For industrial and engineering subjects, the *Proceedings* of various professional societies usually have annual indexes of publications in their fields. Also helpful in this area are the following:

Dalton, Blanche H., *Sources of Engineering Information*. Listing of abstracts and digests services, periodical articles, reference books, etc.

Engineering Index. Author-subject index to periodicals in engineering fields, covering 1884 to the present.

Science Abstracts. Section A covers physics; Section B covers electrical engineering.

Applied Science and Technology Index (formerly *Industrial Arts Index*). Index of industrial and trade subjects, monthly, covering 1913 to the present.

There are also specialized bibliographies available in many fields. Examples would include these pertinent to space technology:

Literature of Space Science and Exploration, compiled by Mildred Benton (U.S. Naval Research Bibliography #13), September, 1958. Available through Office of Technical Services, U.S. Department of Commerce, Washington 25, D.C. Lists books, journals, government research reports, etc., covering 1903 to June, 1958.

Technical Translations, compiled and translated by the Office of Technical Services. Available on subscription—$12.00 per year. Semimonthly directory of translations of technical literature, incorporating *Translation Monthly* of the Special Libraries Association.

Bibliography of Space Medicine, compiled by Charles A. Roos. Available from Director, National Library of Medicine, U.S. Public Health Service, Washington, D.C. Covers space medicine from beginnings to 1958: journals, reports, holdings of U.S. Air Force Office of Scientific Research Library.

An Airpower Bibliography, 1955-1956. Available from Air University, Maxwell Field, Alabama. Includes airpower literature in books, periodicals, talks, interviews, and documents.

Technical journals frequently mention publication of specialized bibliographies pertinent to their fields. A list of typical general and specialized bibliographical aids follows:

GUIDES AND BIBLIOGRAPHIES

Bibliographic Index: A Cumulative Bibliography of Bibliographies. New York: Wilson, 1938 and later.

Coman, Edwin T. *Sources of Business Information*. New York: Prentice-Hall, 1949.

Williams, Cecil B., and Allan H. Stevenson. *A Research Manual*. New York: Harper, 1951.

Winchell, Constance M. *Guide to Reference Books*. Chicago: American Library Association, periodically revised.

ENCYCLOPEDIAS: SPECIALIZED

Encyclopedia of Chemical Technology. New York: Interscience Encyclopedia, 1947 and later.

Encyclopedia of the Social Sciences. New York: Macmillan, 1948, 8 vols.

Hutchinson's Technical and Scientific Encyclopedia. New York: Macmillan, 1936, 4 vols.

GENERAL INDEXES

Leidy, W. Philip. *A Popular Guide to Government Publications*. New York: Columbia University Press, 1953 and later.

United States Catalog: Books in Print. New York: Wilson, 1928. Supplements, called *Cumulative Book Index,* issued since 1928.

United States Government Publications, Catalog and Subject Guide. Washington, D.C.: Government Printing Office, 1895 and later.

EXAMPLES OF PROBLEMS IN LIBRARY RESEARCH[1]

1. In 1957, the early warning radar system known as DEW Line was established. A popular aviation magazine described the event under title of "DEW Line adds 100 Minutes Warning." What was that article?

    Klass, P. J. DEW Line adds 100 minutes warning. *Aviation Week,* 67:100 (Sept. 16, 1957) . (The answer is given here in the form commonly used in bibliographies—author, title, volume, page numbers, and date.)

    Reader's Guide to Periodical Literature

2. Four Russian scientists in 1957 described a "two-crystal neutron spectrometer" in an article. Locate the article.

    Bykov, V. N., S. I. Vinogradov, V. A. Ledvik, and V. S. Golovkin. A two-crystal neutron spectrometer. *Kristallografiya,* 2:634-638 (May, 1957) .

    Science Abstracts, Section A, 1958.

[1] Compiled by Jane Forgotson, former Supervising Science and Technology Librarian, Los Angeles State College.

3. Gages for measuring thickness of metals have been developed which employ ultrasonics. A gage of this type was described in an article published in 1957 and titled "Portable thickness gage for industry." Where was the article published?

Rybb, S. A. Portable thickness gage for industry. *Canadian Metal.*, 20:66-69 (April, 1957).

Engineering Index, 1957.

b. Reading Notes

Take full notes on everything you read during a search of the literature on a problem. It is a good idea to have two kinds of notes: bibliography cards, describing books or articles, and note cards, describing the contents of the books or articles. Some people use 3 by 5 cards, others use large notebooks. Use whatever form is fastest and most convenient for you, but make sure it is consistent for the sake of your filing system. Suggestions for making note cards and examples of notes in summary, paraphrase, and quotation are given in the following sections.

Rapid Reading

It will help you to read faster and take notes better if you understand that a book or article is not very different from a report. In the following chapters we will discuss how a report is put together and where its various parts are located. Later on, we will also examine the structure of paragraphs and sentences to show how they can be used to carry your meaning accurately and logically. As you become familiar with some of the techniques used for these purposes you will also find yourself noticing how other writers use them. Your ability to read faster, with better understanding, and to take notes more easily will follow as a matter of course. For the present, however, a brief preview is in order.

When you pick up a book or article for the first time, do not waste effort by starting to read word for word. Look over the book first: look at the preface or introduction to see what the author intended to do and how he planned to do it. This way you can learn his real subject, his purpose, and his intended audience. Next, look at the table of contents to find out what the book contains. (Keep referring to the table of contents when you read the text. It will help you to see where you have been, where you are, and where you are going.) Then flip through the book as a whole to see if there are summaries of the content. Most books, as well as articles, contain summaries of one form or another. Chapters are sometimes summarized, either at the beginning or the end. Articles are often summarized in what

---

Library call number   Subject or **Category**
                                                Key Word

     AUTHOR'S NAME

     TITLE OF BOOK OR ARTICLE
        For Book: include place of publication
                    publisher
                    year of publication
        For Article: include also title of periodical,
                    volume number (and year)
                    page numbers of article

Bibliography Card

Author and Brief Title   Subject or **Category**
                                                Key Word

     Notes can be of three types:

Page   1. Summary (one or two sentences)
numbers
in left   2. Paraphrase—including more detail than
margin   Summary

              3. Quotation (in quotation marks)—the
                 author's own words <u>accurately</u>

Note Card

```
┌─────────────────────────────────────────────────┐
│  243.523                    Toroballistics        │
│  F500t                                            │
│                                                   │
│     Frank, Claude D.                              │
│                                                   │
│     Toroballistic Theory, 4th ed.                 │
│                                                   │
│     New York: Prudent Press, 1908                 │
│                                                   │
│     pp. 437 - 546 on legalistic works             │
│                                                   │
└─────────────────────────────────────────────────┘
```

Bibliography Card for Book

```
┌─────────────────────────────────────────────────┐
│  203.7¼                     Toroballistics        │
│                                                   │
│     Frank, Claude D.                              │
│                                                   │
│     "Variables in Toroballistics"                 │
│                                                   │
│     Production Planning, July, 1960, 16:306       │
│                                                   │
│                                                   │
│                                                   │
└─────────────────────────────────────────────────┘
```

Bibliography Card for Periodical

is called a "deck," a two- or three-line headline. Often the second paragraph of an article contains a summary, and frequently the concluding paragraph also summarizes. Most technical articles feature an abstract or summary separated from the text.

When you have a summary view of what the book contains, you should try to discover how it is organized and why it is organized that way. There are four very common patterns of organization:

1. *Psychological.* More common in "literature" than in reports or textbooks, this type of organization is built upon psychological factors of interest or emotion. Usually, it proceeds from the specific to the general: from actual cases to generalizations that may be drawn from such cases. Typical examples of this

pattern are the fables of Aesop or the writings of Dr. Norman Vincent Peale.

2. *Structural.* This type of organization is based on how the parts of the subject are related in space: east to west, left to right, up to down, in to out, etc. A geography book or a travel book is based upon such relationships, but so are books on subjects like astronomy, architecture, and plant design. A typical example of a book using this pattern is Cecilia Payne-Gaposchkin's *Stars in the Making* (Cambridge: Harvard University Press, 1952). Another example is Rachel Carson's *The Sea Around Us* (New York: Oxford University Press, 1950).

3. *Chronological.* This is perhaps the most common pattern of organization, simply based on the question: "What happened . . . and what happened next?" Like history texts, the books that use this pattern commonly talk about what happened first, what next, and so on. But sometimes this pattern may appear disguised as "old" compared with "new" or "before and after." Typical examples would include the *Autobiography* of Benjamin Franklin and his *Poor Richard's Almanac.*

4. *Logical.* This pattern is most common in textbooks in the various scientific fields, where a subject is broken down into classifications (sorts of things) and analyses (how parts are related). A book on zoology is perhaps the best example of how this pattern is employed: animals are classified in increasingly smaller groups in terms of similarities and differences. A typical example of a popular book using this pattern is George Gamow, *One Two Three Infinity* (New York: Mentor, 1947) which gives a picture of the universe by discussing speculations current in various scientific fields.

A clue to both the pattern of organization and a summary view of a textbook can be found in the headings and subheadings for each chapter. When only major headings are given in the table of contents, it is still possible to get a summary view and an idea of organization by flipping through the pages and looking at all the headings. These will show how the subject matter is put together, how the parts are connected and follow each other, and especially what the chief point of each section is. Theoretically, everything in the section will bear upon the chief point, in the nature of supporting material. Often you will find that the sup-

porting material is further divided by subheadings into classes
of relative subordination. Headings are thus clues to help you
distinguish the important from the unimportant—a big help
when you are pressed for time.

Reading for Summarizing

The starting point for *reading,* as opposed to *looking at,* a
book or article is, of course, the title. Just as when you prepared
your target statement (Chapter 2), you can turn the title of the
book into a question. Then you can read quickly looking for
answers. Without a target in view, you can easily read buckshot
fashion and notice details rather than major ideas. What is true
for the book is true for each chapter; each chapter heading and
each subheading may be put into question form. In most textbooks, each paragraph usually begins with a topic sentence—
which can also be turned into a question. And within the paragraph, as we will see later, there are supporting sentences to answer that question.

Summarizing

Assuming then that the article or book you are reading is
well organized (and sometimes even when it is not well organized), you can take notes in summary form by following this
procedure:

1. Look for the over-all view.
    a. Rephrase the title as a question and use it as a reference point
       —relate everything you read to it.
    b. Look at the preface and the table of contents to see what the
       real subject is, how much of it is to be covered, what the pur-
       pose of the book is, and for what level of reader the book is
       intended.
    c. Look for summaries of what the author considers to be impor-
       tant.
2. Read and (unless it is a library book) underline.
    a. Underline key headings and number subheadings if they are
       not already numbered or distinguished by letters.
    b. Underline target statements and supporting sentences.
    c. Avoid underlining unimportant, parenthetical, nonessential
       information.
3. Write out underlined passages in your own words.

a. Begin with the title in the form of a leading question, or with the target statement for the whole book in the form of a question.
b. Follow the author's sequence.
c. Emphasize what he emphasizes.
d. Be accurate in copying facts and figures.
e. Eliminate all but the most important illustrations or examples and use general statements to cover lengthy, complex data.
f. Use a simple, straightforward style that ties the ideas together in smooth connections.

Kinds of Summarizing

The kind of summary described above is sometimes called a paraphrase. It is particularly useful when taking notes for information rather than authority or testimony. Notes that are to be used to corroborate your findings or judgments should, of course, be taken verbatim, enclosed with quotation marks, and accurately referenced.

There is, however, another type of summary widely used in report writing. Although it is sometimes called a "summary," "abstract" is a better term. The abstract describes what a book or an article *contains* rather than what it says. It tells what information is available. To indicate the difference between a summary and an abstract, here is a quotation from an article by Harold J. Von Beckh, "Human Reaction During Flight to Acceleration," which appeared in *Aerospace Medicine,* 30 (1959), 393:

A prospective Manhigh III subject was selected for this experiment. He went without sleep for 48 hours. After a full breakfast, which increased his sleepiness, he entered the rear cockpit of our experimental F94C aircraft. He unhooked his headset at 11,000 feet so as not to be disturbed by the conversation of the pilot, tower, and experimenter. Twenty-five minutes after takeoff the subject fell asleep, leaning against the right side of the cockpit. A string was fixed on his left wrist, which the pilot could pull to awaken him. The pilot avoided any rough maneuvers.

The aircraft was then flown in a zero G trajectory and the subject was awakened. His first impressions upon awakening were that his arms and legs "were floating away from him" so that he felt a desperate need to pull them back toward his body to maintain some sort of normal posture. He tried to hold on to the canopy and some part of the cockpit. He could not orient himself. He is a pilot of over 500 jet hours and had not experienced such pronounced disorientation previously.

Now consider this *paraphrase* of the passage:

What are the impressions of a subject awakened during a weightless state? An experienced jet pilot awakened in a weightless state during an experiment said that his first impressions were a desperate need to capture his "floating" arms and legs to maintain normal posture. His disorientation was more pronounced than he had ever experienced in 500 hours of jet flight time.

And now consider this *abstract* of the same passage:

Dr. Von Beckh describes an experiment investigating the impressions of a subject awakened during the weightless state. The subject experienced disorientation.

Summarizing for a Purpose

It is important to realize that the passage could be summarized in several different ways, depending on your purpose in making note of it. For example, if you wanted to emphasize *how the experiment was performed,* the summary would read something like this:

How can we investigate the impressions of a subject awakening in a weightless state? A subject was induced into deep sleep in an experimental F94C aircraft 25 minutes after takeoff. The aircraft was then flown in a zero G trajectory and the pilot awakened the subject by pulling a string attached to his wrist.

An abstract of the same information, taken for the same purpose, would read:

Dr. Von Beckh describes the experimental method he used to obtain the impressions of a subject awakened during weightlessness in an experimental F94C aircraft.

The problem in summarizing for note-taking purposes, then, is selecting the highlights and supporting details most appropriate to your needs. If you are concerned only with recording what information is available, an abstract should do the job. If, on the other hand, the information is the important thing, an extended summary is in order.

3. DIRECT INQUIRY

a. Interview

When information has not been published, it may be necessary to interview people to obtain it. Good interviewing requires your best professional manner: politeness, objectivity, and alertness. There are two chief methods—direct and indirect. In direct interviewing, the following directions are important:

1. Prepare questions beforehand.

   Who?   Know your man before you get there. Make inquiries about him.

   What's the subject?   Bone up on it, so you understand the language.

   What time?   Make an appointment and keep it.

   Where?   Note location and how to get there.

   What objective?   State your purpose directly—don't waste his time.

   What specific points?   Prepare more than you will use.

2. Take your time.

   Lead into the interview with some kind of introduction, including some idea of why you are conducting it, what you hope to do with the information. Do not rush the man in his answers. Keep quiet and let him do the answering. *Take accurate notes.*

3. Do not argue or contradict.

   He may not be right but—at least so far as he is concerned—he is never wrong. Be polite. Then at the end of the interview, review your notes with him, and let him see for himself that he is wrong.

4. Finish up and leave.

The difference between direct and indirect interviewing techniques is indicated by the terms "structured" and "unstructured." The direct "structured" interview follows the sequence of your prepared questions. That is why it is important to prepare your questions beforehand and to try to keep your friend on the track (politely). The indirect "unstructured" interview, however, lets him guide the talk. You begin with a few provocative questions to give him some idea of what you want him to talk about. Then you let him talk. When he stops talking, you ask a question designed to keep him thinking along the lines you would like him to follow. This usually amounts to changing a statement he has just made into a question, or simply repeating his last words in the form of a question.

Indirect interviewing is helpful when you want to know what lies behind a man's thoughts. The theory is: if you let him talk long enough, he will finally tell you what is really on his mind. This explains why the technique is basic to depth interviewing in "motivational" research. Ordinarily, however, it is too time-consuming for industrial report purposes, where the objective is to get the information quickly and accurately. Where the problem is to get the man to tell you something he doesn't want to tell you, indirect interviewing is a last resort.

The important rule in interviewing is to take *accurate notes.* The same techniques of summarizing apply here as in library research. The big difference is that you can seldom refer back to your man the way you can to a book. This is particularly important to remember on field trips away from your base of operations. It is the reason some skilled interviewers insist on reading their notes back to the people they have interviewed immediately after the interview, even at the risk of seeming foolish. The rereading serves not only to check accuracy, but also to stimulate the man interviewed to think of something he may have forgotten. The professional approach to this rereading is to propose a summary of the "discussion."

EXAMPLE OF INTERVIEW—FROM NOTES TO WRITE-UP

Who? Dr. Horace Kohler
Subject. Status of research in molecular diseases
Time. 11:30 A.M.-1:00 P.M., 20 May 58
Place. Cal Tech labs—Zoo 357
Objective. State of art report
Specific points. 1. Work of Yung and Lee on nutrinos (Nobel prize).
          2. Measurement of hemoglobin molecule.

3. Transmission of molecular diseases of this kind.
4. Extent of molecular diseases.
5. Cause of molecular diseases.

NOTES

1. Minute nutrinos have left-handed, right-handed properties. For this, awarded Nobel within a year—symbol of importance of science in modern world. (Note: this omitted in write-up.)
2. Measured precisely since early 1920's—even behavior. Can now measure hemoglobin molecule very precisely.
3. Genetically only—"sports."
4. Hundreds—12 definite from sports.
5. Mutation from some agent, e.g., "cosmic rays."

WRITE-UP

The work of Yung and Lee which won them the Nobel Prize disclosed that nutrinos behave like little propellers—some left-handed, others right-handed. This work in the submicroscopic world is indicative of progress made in the field since the early 1920's, when work with molecular measurement got under way. Today it is possible to measure hemoglobin atoms as well. Dr. Kohler and his staff are currently concerned with molecular diseases of hemoglobin and have already shown that they are transmitted genetically. There are, in fact, now about twelve definitely recognizable diseases of human hemoglobin, all derivative of "sports" created by some mutating agent such as cosmic rays. Dr. Kohler suspects there are hundreds of molecular diseases. His work is now concerned with whether some are responsible for mental disease and deficiencies.

EXAMPLE OF INTERVIEW AND OBSERVATION COMBINED

Excerpt from trip report. Purpose was to survey plastic production facilities nationwide.

This company does all of its own vacuum forming. Numerous parts were being formed while we were in the plastic shops. They do a particularly good job of vacuum forming and have very good tools.

They are also doing extensive work with acrylics and have developed a process whereby optical correction is not necessary for plexiglas canopies. This has meant considerable savings to the company.

We were given several reasons for their entry into the plastics business on such a large scale: (1) to obtain high quality parts;

(2) to maintain quality control; (3) to achieve cost savings; (4) to adapt latest processing and manufacturing techniques; (5) to avoid paying for subcontractors' equipment every time a contract was let. The company obtains what it wants, when it wants it, and is considering expanding their already excellent shops.

Management appears to be well informed and aware of pitfalls prevalent in the plastics industry. Personnel are industrious, capable, and farsighted. The state of the art here is far above any others seen.

b. Questionnaire

Preparing questionnaires is a specialized art best left to the specialists.[2] In case of emergency, however, the following instructions may be of some help:

1. Questions should be focused on one factor at a time.
2. Questions should be "closed," that is, they should allow "yes" or "no" answers or some simple response such as: "too much, more than enough, just about right, not enough, too little."
3. Questions should be clear on first reading and easy to answer with a minimum of study or reflection.
4. Questions should be phrased in simple, unemotional language, avoiding slanted or suggestive wording.
5. Questions should be arranged in logical sequence, beginning with the simplest questions (name, address, age, and so forth) and maintaining easy continuity and connection from question to question.
6. Questions on any given questionnaire should usually be limited to no more than 15.

Some sample questions for a simple questionnaire are given below:

Are employees permitted coffee-making facilities?
Are employees permitted coffee breaks?
Are employees permitted to drink coffee between coffee breaks?
Are employees permitted to leave the plant during coffee breaks?
Are employees required to sign out when leaving for coffee breaks?
Are employees required to make up time overstayed on coffee breaks?

[2] See Norman B. Sigband, *Effective Report Writing*, New York: Harper, 1960, pp. 71-84.

c. Correspondence

Letters and memoranda[3] are a common source of information, and it is professionally appropriate to write letters requesting specific data as well as general information. Answering letters of inquiry is a routine part of business and professional life, with most major firms having a policy of answering such letters within five days after receiving them. Procter and Gamble, for example, maintains a department whose sole responsibility is to handle such correspondence, and it is company policy to answer every letter received.

The rules of good business and social correspondence (accuracy, brevity, dignity) apply to technical letters and memoranda as well. Technical correspondence is perhaps more formal and efficient, with a tendency to get right to the point without any attempt at "folksy" friendliness. But the basic pattern is the same:

1. The first paragraph, considered the introduction, tells why the letter is being written and summarizes its chief point.
2. The second paragraph, or the body, discusses or explains the chief point, and may be expanded into other, supporting, paragraphs if the point requires additional explanation.
3. The closing paragraph, the conclusion, sums up the discussion and closes with (a) a request or recommendation for specific action, (b) a summary of how the discussion is to be interpreted, or (c) a promise of additional communication.

You will find that most firms and government agencies are eager to assist legitimate research projects when they are able to do so. Often, however, the information you request may be classified secret in the interests of national security. Or such information may be considered "proprietary," or for internal dissemination only. It is important that you record the fact that the information does exist even though you cannot obtain it. For it may some day be available for your use, or at least the use of future researchers.

The correspondence that follows is intended to show charac-

---

[3] Letters and memoranda differ chiefly in format and function rather than content. See Table I, p. 30.

teristic replies to a typical letter of inquiry. In this case, the requested information was so new that many agencies had not yet heard about the field. Nevertheless, as you will see, they were able to suggest sources that eventually lead to the company working on the specific problem that interested the report writer.

THE ORIGINAL LETTER

COMMUNICATION RESEARCH CENTER
Los Angeles 32, Calif.

November 25, 19—

Press Department
Soviet Embassy
Washington 9, D.C.

Gentlemen:

We are conducting a survey of international research on use of ceramic coatings for aero-space vehicles in connection with the Geophysical Year.

We are specifically interested in the effects of cosmic radiation on ceramics or cermets, and would appreciate your help in calling to our attention any known work in this field.

Since our Geophysical Year activities are scheduled to conclude on 15 March 1959, we would appreciate your assistance in expediting our correspondence with possible informants.

Very truly yours,
COMMUNICATION RESEARCH CENTER

Samuel Adams
Director

REPLY 1 (A FORM LETTER)

Press Department
Embassy of the
UNION OF SOVIET SOCIALIST REPUBLICS
1706 Eighteenth Street, N.W.
Washington 9, D.C.

1 December 19—

Mr. Samuel Adams
Communication Research Center
Los Angeles 32, California

Dear Mr. Adams:

We regret that we do not have the information at hand to comply with your specific request, and suggest that you address your inquiry directly to the following:

State Committee on Cultural Relations with Foreign Countries
9 Kalinin Street
Moscow, USSR.

Thank you for your inquiry.

Sincerely yours,

Press Department

REPLY 2

S.C.C.R.F.C.
9 Kalinin St.
Moscow U.S.S.R.

19.12.58

Mr. Samuel Adams
Communication Research Center
Los Angeles 32, California
U.S.A.

Dear Mr. Adams:

In answer to your request may we inform you that all scientific and technical papers, articles, reports, communications, etc., published in Soviet publications are abstracted in *Journal of Abstracts* which you can get in all important libraries of the U.S.A.

Under separate cover we are sending you a catalog of Soviet scientific journals. In this catalog on page 34 is a list of the series of *Journal of Abstracts* and on page 62 the addresses of firms in the U.S.A. through which you can subscribe to all Soviet scientific periodicals.

Committee for Cultural Relations
with Foreign Countries

REPLY TO SIMILAR INQUIRY (BRITISH)

BRITISH INFORMATION SERVICES
45 Rockefeller Plaza
New York 20, N.Y.

1 December 19—

Dear Mr. Adams:

Your letter of November 15 addressed to the British Embassy has been referred to us for reply.

Although the Royal Observatory at Herstmonceux, Sussex, the Imperial College, London, the University of Bristol, and Makerere College, Uganda, have been studying the incidence and properties of cosmic rays as a part of the United Kingdom's contributions to the International Geophysical Year, we know of no special British Government studies the results of which have been published. We are therefore unable to provide you with any information which would be of assistance to your research into the possible materials for the shielding of rockets from cosmic rays.

Very truly yours

Constance Gray
Reference Section

Mr. Samuel Adams
Communication Research Center
Los Angeles 32, California

REPLY TO SIMILAR INQUIRY (U.S.A.)

COSMIC DYNAMICS CORPORATION
General Offices
San Diego 12, California

December 31, 19—

Mr. Samuel Adams
Communication Research Center
Los Angeles 32, California

Dear Mr. Adams:

This will acknowledge your inquiry of November 15 in connection with your research in the field of ceramics. We have checked not only our manufacturing research and development people in the San Diego Division but also the Cosmic Dynamics Research Lab in order to try to help you.

It seems, however, that we have no information that would be of help to you in your research. I would suggest you direct an inquiry to the director of the Space Race Propulsion Laboratory at Portland for assistance. If they cannot help you, I am sure they will be able to direct you to some organization which can.

Thank you for thinking of Cosmic Dynamics and I am sorry we are unable to help you.

Sincerely yours,

Andrew Armsworth
Research Director

REPLY TO SIMILAR INQUIRY (U.S.A. [2])

SPACE RACE PROPULSION LABORATORY
1962 High Street
Portland, Oregon

January 12, 19—

Mr. Samuel Adams
Communication Research Center
Los Angeles 32, California

Dear Mr. Adams:

I regret that the press of new-year duties has so long delayed my reply to your January 3, 1959, letter.

We do not have any material on hand bearing on the subject you mention. We have been interested in measuring cosmic rays rather than in fending them off.

You might write for information to the Physics Department of the State University of Altadena, the National Aeronautics and Space Administration, or the Missile Division of Norumbega Aviation Company.

Sincerely yours,

John Alden
Director of Information

REPLY TO SIMILAR INQUIRY (U.S.A. [3])

NORUMBEGA AVIATION COMPANY
Missile Division
18118 Norumbega Park Drive
Erie, Wisconsin

2 March 19—

Mr. Samuel Adams
Communication Research Center
Los Angeles 32, California

Dear Mr. Adams:

Some weeks ago, you wrote Norumbega requesting some information on ceramics or cermets which might be useful on space vehicles. Unfortunately, the letter was mislaid in its routing from our main office to this Division, hence the delay in answering.

This division has done considerable research on the subject, but all of the reports and papers which have been prepared are classified and therefore are not available for distribution. Some unclassified papers have been published in such magazines as Jet Propulsion and Ceramic Industry, which are available in the various libraries, and these might be of help to you. Additionally, I understand the State University of Altadena has done some work in the field and may have some readily available material.

As you can understand, it is not possible for us to prepare a special unclassified report for you. However, if you have any specific questions, send them to us and we will attempt to find the answers for you.

Cordially,
NORUMBEGA AVIATION COMPANY
Missile Division

Peter Waldhorn
Public Relations

PW:rhs

Whether you collect your information by means of tests, literature search, or direct inquiry you will find it helpful to compile your notes in some kind of system. Many people use handy 3 x 5 index cards kept in cardboard files easily obtainable at a stationery shop. Others prefer larger cards which enable them to include more information. Some people use cards that are color-coded, with different colors denoting different subject areas. The advantage of cards of course is that they can be shuffled around and laid out in many different arrangements. Nevertheless, many people prefer to collect their notes in looseleaf notebooks and shuffle pages instead. Whatever system you use is better than haphazardly taking notes on the backs of envelopes or matchbook covers and letting them pile up in a desk drawer. A note worth taking is a note worth keeping . . . carefully.

In general, then, take notes on everything—tests, reading, inquiries, even conversations—that may be of use. Take notes on the spot—or as soon as you can do it conveniently and (in the case of interviews) unobtrusively. Take more notes than you think you will need, but do not take notes simply for the purpose of taking notes; keep your purpose and audience in mind. Throw nothing away, at least until the report has been finished, circulated, and commented upon by those for whom it was prepared. Even then, keep your notes on file if you can. You never know when they may come in handy again. Some of them probably could not be duplicated without a great deal of effort. Some of them are irreplacable. Replacing even simple notes would require your going back down a long road again, and you still have a long road ahead. Remember, any schoolboy can accumulate notes. Knowing what to do with them separates the men from the boys.

PRACTICE PROBLEMS: COLLECTING INFORMATION

1. Compare the figures given below with the most recent statistics issued by the Bureau of the Census. Try to establish the patterns of change since 1950, particularly with respect to geography.

City	Population
New York	12,831,914
Chicago	5,475,535
Los Angeles	4,339,225
Philadelphia	3,660,676

City	Population
Detroit	2,973,019
Boston	2,354,457
San Francisco-Oakland	2,214,249
Pittsburgh	2,205,544
St. Louis	1,673,467
Washington	1,457,601

2. The following figures represent sales of large motor trucks by four major manufacturers last month. Summarize these figures in a statement or two that will be incorporated into a report to top management. Management is currently considering whether to diversify into truck manufacturing.

Manufacturer and Model		No. of Units	Net Sales
Alpha	500A	5	$866,000
	500E	0	
	680F	6	
	720	0	
Beta	18	5	$1,988,000
	33	4	
	35	18	
	50	0	
	65	4	
	95	9	
Gamma	150	57	$4,622,000
	172	279	
	175	9	
	180	13	
	182	18	
	210	10	
	310	18	
Delta	L4	2	$45,000
Epsilon	18	27	$1,196,000
	22	11	
	23	3	
	23-A	12	
	24	7	
	24-A	17	
	25	5	
Totals		539	$8,717,000

3. Summarize the following facts and figures to suit three different purposes: (1) To show the historical development of the industry. (2) To explain why the industry grew so swiftly. (3) To describe the scope of the industry in 1959.

During World War II, these were developed: LORAN navigation systems, the proximity fuse, new bombsight equipment, and improvements in sonar detection and radar systems.

We learned to use electronics for counting and calculating, and we evolved swift control devices for aircraft and weapons.

We spent $7.5 billion on military purchase of electronics and communications equipment between 1941 and 1945, and employed 500,000 people in the electronics industry. In 1949, military purchases accounted for less than 20 percent of sales.

During 1950-1953 the electronics industry doubled, with military production increasing five times and accounting for one-half the $5.2 billion industry volume. About 40 percent of the estimated 575,000 employed in the industry were working on military production.

Total production in 1959 increased seven percent over 1958 in the electronics industry. Total production in 1959 was $4.7 billion.

Nearly three-fourths of the total dollar volume of electronics production is concentrated in seven states—New York, Illinois, California, New Jersey, Pennsylvania, Massachusetts, and Indiana. New York leads with over 31 percent of the total. California is second with over 16 percent. About 760,000 are now employed in electronic manufacturing—about one-seventh are engineers. The military market absorbs about 51 percent of total sales.

4. Summarize the following three reports[4] into one paragraph not exceeding seventy-five words.

REPORT A

1. *The Drop.* A single atomic bomb, the first weapon of its type, exploded over Hiroshima at 0815. Most of the industrial workers had already reported to work, but many workers were en route and nearly all the school children were at work in the open on the program of building-removal to provide fire breaks

---

[4] These reports are based on "Effects of Atomic Bombs on Hiroshima and Nagasaki," *U.S. Strategic Bombing Survey,* Government Printing Office, 1946.

and to disperse valuables to the country. The attack came 5 minutes after the all clear from a previous alert.

2. *Complete Destruction.* The bomb exploded slightly northwest of the center of the city. Because of this accuracy and the
flat terrain and circular shape of the city, Hiroshima was extensively and uniformly devastated. Practically the entire densely or
moderately built-up portion of the city was leveled by blast and
swept by fire. Fires sprang up almost simultaneously over the
wide flat area around the center of the city and drew in air from
all directions. The inrush of air easily overcame the natural
ground wind, which had a velocity of only about 5 mph. This fire
wind attained a maximum velocity of 30 to 40 mph 2 to 3 hours
after the explosion. The fire wind and the symmetry of the
built-up center of the city gave a roughly circular shape to the
area which was almost completely burned out.

3. *Unprecedented Casualties.* The surprise, the collapse of
many buildings, and the fire contributed to an unprecedented
casualty rate. Seventy to eighty thousand people were killed, or
missing and presumed dead; and an equal number were injured.
The magnitude of casualties is set in relief by a comparison with
the Tokyo fire raid of 9-10 March 1945, in which, though nearly
16 square miles were destroyed, the number killed was no larger
and fewer people were injured.

REPORT B

At 8:15 A.M., a single atomic bomb, the first of its type ever
used at a target, exploded over the city of Hiroshima. Just about
the entire densely or moderately built-up portion of the city was
leveled by blast and swept by fire. Most of the workers were already at work, but many were en route and nearly all the school
children and some workers were busy in the open on the program
of building-removal to provide fire breaks and disperse valuables
to the country. Because no warning was received and because the
people were indifferent to small groups of planes, the explosion
was almost a complete surprise; thus, few people had taken shel-
ter. Many were caught in the open; most of the rest were in
flimsy homes or commercial establishments.

The bomb exploded slightly northwest of the center of the city.
Because of this accuracy and the flat terrain and circular shape of
the city, Hiroshima was uniformly and extensively laid waste.

A fire storm, which has occurred infrequently in other conflagrations, developed in Hiroshima—fires springing up almost at the same time over the wide flat area around the center of the city drew in air from all directions. The inrush of air easily overcame the natural ground wind, which had a velocity of only about 5 miles per hour. The fire wind attained a maximum velocity of 30 to 40 miles per hour 2 to 3 hours after the explosion. The fire wind and the symmetry of the built-up center of the city gave a roughly circular shape to the 4.4 square miles which were almost completely burned out. The surprise, the collapse of many buildings, and the conflagration contributed to an unprecedented casualty rate.

REPORT C

One sunny summer morning, shortly after the "All Clear" from an earlier alert, the bustling Japanese metropolis of Hiroshima was devastated by the first nuclear bomb ever used against a target. The local inhabitants, careless from constant exposure to peril from the air, almost indifferent to small formations of aircraft, and taken almost entirely by surprise, were mostly caught in the open without protection of any sort or in homes or commercial establishments of the most flimsy construction. The resulting casualty rate was without precedent—in the number who were killed; in the number whose bodies were never recovered and were presumed dead; and in the number (equally large) who were injured. (By comparison the punishing Tokyo fire raid of March 9 and 10, 1945, took a larger toll of fatalities but far fewer were injured.)

Damage to property was equally severe. The bomb exploded slightly to the north and west of the geographical center of Hiroshima on the sixth of August, 1945. Since the layout of Hiroshima was roughly circular, the level central areas of the city where buildings were most heavily concentrated were uniformly laid waste by the blast of the explosion. Immediately after the explosion, myriad small fires sprang up; the heat which rose from these fires drew in air from the flat lands around the center of the municipality. The result was a roaring fire storm, a phenomenon not often met with, which completed the destruction of the hapless city.

5. Summarize the eyewitness report given below into one para-

graph, not exceeding seventy-five words, describing the collapse of the bridge for an audience of specialists in bridge design.

FALL OF TACOMA NARROWS BRIDGE

Collapse of the Tacoma Narrows Bridge near Tacoma, Washington, on November 7, 1940, was one of the sensational episodes in engineering history. It had been opened to traffic only four months before, and had a central span of 2800 feet, east and west side spans of 1100 feet each. A complete report of the collapse has been published in *Bulletin of the Agricultural and Mechanical College of Texas* (4th series, vol. XV, no. 1), from which the following eyewitness statements have been drawn:

9:30 A.M.   There is a southerly wind with recorded velocity of 42 mph. The bridge has, for some hours now, developed vertical wave motions. This has been experienced previously on this bridge. Present motion now has sufficient amplitude to attract special attention. The wind is striking at a quartering angle. And now the bridge is vibrating in eight or more segments. Frequency of vibration is 36 cycles per minute with a double amplitude of about 3 feet. The cables must be vibrating in phase with one another, as they have done in the past. At least the bridge floor has not twisted.

10:00 A.M.   The motion has changed. The main span is now vibrating in two segments. A node at midspan has a frequency of 14 cycles per minute. The cables are vibrating out of phase with one another. The roadway is twisting and warping: one side of the floor is going up while the other side goes down. Now the frequency has changed from 14 to 12 cycles per minute. The deck is tilting to more than 30 degrees each way from the horizontal. The double amplitude of the waves is reaching 28 feet. There is little lateral motion of the bridge. Maximum value at midspan is about 2 feet. They say there is more violent motion on the west than on the east half.

10:30 A.M.   A truck and a car are crossing the bridge. The truck driver and his companion have just abandoned it. Now it has been overturned. They are being helped off the bridge. The driver of the car has left it, too. He says the roadway on the north side seemed to drop suddenly, spinning his car to the south curb. Then the tilting reversed and he was spun toward the north curb. So he gave up and crawled on all fours across to the east end.

11:00 A.M.   There she goes! A panel of floor adjacent to the expansion joint just east of mid-span just dropped out. Now a 600-foot section of floor is going. There is a gap now from a point 300 feet west of mid-span to within 500 feet of the west tower. Suspenders are breaking progressively from east to west. The north stiffening girder is gone. It has turned upside down and is swinging onto the south cable. Floor beams are successively tearing loose. The whole thing is collapsing. The tower tops are falling shoreward about 16 or 17 feet.

6. Summarize the information in this letter to meet one of four purposes: (1) Report that the investigation is in progress. (2) Report that the crash occurred. (3) Report the cause of the crash. (4) Make recommendations to prevent future crashes.

RICHELIEU AIRCRAFT COMPANY
Farlow Field Road N.
Richelieu, Missouri

21 December 19—

Air Safety Association
Airways Building
Washington 6, D.C.

Attention: Sherman Williams, Director

Subject: Preliminary Report—YB-16 Crash, 22 November 1959, Farlow Field, Mo.

Gentlemen:

Complying with your request of 23 November 1959 (your reference 7602), this preliminary report summarizes information pertinent to the YB-16 crash at Farlow Field, Missouri, 22 November 1959.

The Crash

At 05:42 on 22 November 1959, the YB-16, Number 1439, became airborne on a cross-country flight to evaluate navigation equipment. Almost immediately, control tower personnel noticed a large volume of black smoke issuing from around the port nacelle. The craft appeared to hesitate in mid-air, then began to lose altitude. Approximately 50 seconds after take-off, it struck power lines bordering the airfield and crashed.

Cause

Investigation to date indicates that the crash was caused by several related factors:

1. A study of the wreckage showed that new-type electrical connectors located in the wheel-well had been installed in inverted position. Terminal lugs showed signs of fatigue failure. This could have caused a short circuit in the electrical system and an arcing condition. There is some indication of leakage from an oil line prior to the crash.

2. The pilot says that the port engine had backfired upon take-off, and he immediately noticed a sudden drop in oil pressure. Assuming impending engine failure, he attempted to shut off power to that engine. Before he could do so, he observed a flash of fire in the vicinity of the nacelle. His efforts to contend with the new emergency distracted him from take-off procedure.

Tentative Recommendations

The investigating board offers the following tentative recommendations pending completion of this study:

1. All installations of the new-type connector should be inspected for correct installation.

2. Safety valves should be installed on all models to prevent excessive pressure in the oil system.

3. Means should be provided for extinguishing fires in the wheel-wells.

4. Certification tests of pilots should include some kind of measurement of their ability to cope with emergencies.

Items (1) and (2) should be initiated immediately.

Estimated Completion Date

Final study of this incident should be completed by 1 April 1960. A complete report will be submitted to your office by that date.

Very truly yours,
RICHELIEU AIRCRAFT COMPANY

Ludowick Richelieu, President

7. From these verbatim notes taken during an interview with a famous space scientist, prepare a statement summarizing his proposal.

We'll send out, maybe, all kinds of conditions permitting, one of the nice vehicles of the Army Research Project or the NASA and put a little nuclear explosive on it, and let it go out a big healthy distance, like, let's say, hundred million miles, and then look sharp! This thing will explode and send out the whole electromagnetic spectrum from an X-ray through visible to infrared through radar. These will be emitted in a very sharply defined time instant to an accuracy better than a microsecond. Let's see whether all these signals will arrive at precisely the same time. Physics relativity tells us that no matter whether it's X-rays or visible or radar, light velocity is light velocity and we mean it and there is no deviation of the light velocity whatsoever. We'll have the means to check this statement (the theory of relativity I mean) more than a thousand times better than anybody has checked it before.

8. Prepare a letter to a former employer in which you request a letter recommending you for a position as director of research at Hobgrass Corporation, 1515 Knob Hill Road, Chicago. This will of course require you to summarize for his use a statement of your experience (real or imaginary, as the case may be) pertinent to a position of this sort.

9. Prepare a letter to Webley-Vickers Arms Company, Canute, Ohio, in which you request information about a light-weight, low-cost rocket launcher capable of firing 13 rounds per minute. The launcher must be easily portable by one man and must require a minimum of maintenance. It will be used for weather research balloon vehicles and must therefore be able to withstand extremes of climate in all parts of the world.

10. Prepare a letter to Webley-Vickers in which you attempt to learn: (1) the total number of employees, including the number of research scientists, development engineers, and other technical personnel; (2) previous examples of work and background related to your project; (3) brief description of facilities available for this kind of work; and (4) types of personnel and facility security clearances for secret-level work. Some of this material may be classified.

CHAPTER 4

Designing

After you have your information collected on note cards or in a looseleaf notebook, you can get organized—in the usual sense of the word. You will find it helpful to think about organizing as a three-phase process determining:

1. *Which of your notes you will use?* This involves classification and analysis, or finding out what sorts of things you are dealing with; what are the constituent parts of these things; and how these parts are put together. Then you can select those you need.
2. *What sequence your notes should follow?* This involves shuffling your selected notes in various arrangements so that you can see which sequence will best suit your purpose.
3. *How they will best work together?* This involves choosing an appropriate balance of parts, providing necessary connections, and determining proper emphasis.

The process of organizing along these lines will result in an over-all view of your report, similar to the over-all view you have of a book when you skim through it for the first time.

You already have a preliminary structural design because in the planning stage you prepared a target statement and program plan. In the design stage you will be concerned with constructing the framework, or structural outline, and arranging the parts to meet design requirements determined by your audience and purpose.

1. THE BASIC PATTERN

We can compare the design of a report to the design of a bridge. The span should be designed to bear the full weight of your subject. The span will be supported by pylon-like structural elements. These structural elements in turn will be sustained by supporting elements, more specific, more complex, more technical. The structural elements carry the burden of the message. The supporting elements are explanations, definitions, or examples which reinforce the structural elements.

This pattern of structure-plus-support is common in report writing. It is so familiar, in fact, that you can write nonsense and still seem to be making sense. The following paragraph is constructed on this pattern, and if you read it aloud quickly (and with appropriate dramatic emphasis), your friends will be amazed at your erudition. The opening sentence is the structural element and the other sentences support some aspect of it, along this outline: "How do dipolar nodules achieve inverse reactive current? What are dipolar nodules? How are they used? What effects are achieved? How are these effects achieved?"

Inverse reactive current for unilateral phase detractors is achieved by automatically synchronizing dipolar nodules. These nodules are trammetrically relative with respect to inverse flux introduced in a gravometric field and may be defined as entropic dissimulated matrixes operating in a fluid medium. A typical application would consist of rotating a magnetoregulator in a directance field without recourse to allotropic resonance. In prototype phases, this would have the effect of surreptitiously overcoming pentateuchal marzeltorque. The axial members thus acquire irregular manestetic characteristics that give dipolar modules their properties of nonreversible malleresis. Thus, for example, high velocity psalmanazaric waves coming into contact with synchronized nodules lose weight-strength on the order of $2.78N$ where N is the blipspiel constant divided by the coefficient of ampuscular warp.

Recognizing the distinction between structural and supporting elements will be very helpful in analyzing your notes as well as in designing your report. Do the notes contain major points or supporting examples, definitions, illustrations? When the distinction is clear you can compile your structural points into groups or classes, according to similarities and differences or some other classification. This will give you a basis for analyzing the supporting points.

2. OUTLINES

The usual method of analysis is to outline, just as you did when formulating a target statement. Outlining enables you to break down your structural points into supporting parts, and also to differentiate between the major and secondary parts. The purpose of an outline is to show the relations between the parts and the relations of the parts to the whole subject. In this respect the outline is essential in plotting direction and destination.

If you have already prepared a good target statement, the process of outlining becomes a matter of breaking down that statement into structural and supporting points. Structural points are represented by major headings, supporting points by subordinate headings, according to number or letter systems such as the following:

NUMBER-LETTER SYSTEM

I.
   A.
      1.
         a.
            i.
               (a)
               (b)
            ii.
         b.
      2.
   B.
II.

DECIMAL SYSTEM

  1.
     1.1
        1.11
           1.111
              1.1111
                  1.11111
                  1.11112
              1.1112
           1.112
        1.12
     1.2
  2.

You can then test your notes against the headings to see where they fit. Some of the notes will be coordinates, that is, they will be of equal importance. Others will be subordinates, dependent upon or aspects of one of the coordinates. If an outline does not have a balance of supporting subordinate headings, it will *look* lopsided. Similarly, if an outline consists of only major coordinate headings, you may be expecting structural elements to carry more weight than they can bear without support.

You have a choice of three common types of outline, illustrated below. Choose whichever type is most congenial:

THREE TYPES OF OUTLINES   (Title)

Purpose: To describe the three common types of outline.

  I. Topical outline   (Main Class)
     A. Advantages   (Subclass)
     B. Disadvantages
        1. Crutch
        2. Skimpy

 II. Key word outline   (Coordinate with I and III)
     A. Brief, concise, fast   (Subordinate to II)
     B. Coordinates unelaborated
        1. Omitted details
        2. Risk of forgetting

III. Topic sentence outline is best for writing fast.
   A. Gives coordinates in detail.
   B. Takes time and thought.
      1. You have to think things through first.
      2. You have to worry about expression.

Whatever type of outline you use, observe these rules:

1. Each heading for a main class should be meaningful in itself.
2. All main classes should be equal in importance.
3. Subclasses under any main class should also be equal in importance.
4. Headings should be in similar form—all phrases or all sentences or all participles, etc. (The sample outline shown above was intended to show types rather than appropriate form.)

Remember that an outline is only a guide. It is not a substitute for developing your ideas and thinking them out in detail. In fact, only in exceptional cases will a preliminary outline be in such good shape that it can be used as a final table of contents without considerable modification.

This is not to underestimate the importance of preparing an outline. An outline is absolutely necessary in designing a report, even a brief letter report, because it forces you to think before you write. It enables you to recognize likenesses and differences and form workable categories and subcategories. In short, an outline enables you to see order in chaos. Furthermore, an outline enables you to distinguish the nature of parts within each category and to see them from various points of view. The parts of the human body, for example, may be seen from the point of view of a chemist, a physician, a Hollywood producer, a clothier, a human factors engineer, and so forth. Similarly, the parts of an idea may be seen from a variety of points of view when they are laid out in outline and not influenced by the suggestiveness of discourse.

Finally, an outline provides a testing ground. You can try out different sequences of arrangement. For example, which comes first, "advantages" or "disadvantages?" Do you explain how a thing works before you describe how it is made? Do you describe a thing from the inside out or from the outside in? An outline gives you a chance to determine which arrangement is best suited to your purpose.

3. TYPICAL SEQUENCES

When we were talking about reading notes, we noted the four common patterns of development in books: psychological, structural, chronological, and logical. These patterns are based on sequence of presentation, and their use is determined by the requirements of the book and the point of view of the author. The same patterns are also common in reports. A proposal to a government agency, for example, might well follow a pattern similar to that of a lawyer's plea to a jury (psychological). A report of a survey of land would use a structural pattern. A test report would use a chronological pattern. A report on a search through the literature on a particular subject would use a logical pattern. But there is a common denominator in the patterns when applied to reports: the sequence of presentation follows what is called an inverted pyramid progression.

An inverted pyramid progression simply means a sequence in which the main point is given first, then the supporting points, and then a restatement of the main point. Perhaps you know about this pattern in terms of: "Tell 'em what you're going to tell 'em. Tell 'em. Tell 'em you told 'em." The reasons for using this sequence have already been discussed in Chapter 1, and now we will see some of the ways in which the pattern may be used.

The sequences outlined below are common to reports in business, industry, and government agencies. They are applicable to paragraphs and sections as well as reports in their entirety. Variations within the patterns are, of course, determined by appropriateness, report requirements, and your own needs. They are classified here according to function and in the order in which you would most likely handle them if you were going to include all of them in a report.

I. Description
   A. Device ("Machine" Description)
      1. What is it?
      2. What is it used for?
      3. What does it look like?
      4. How is it made? or What is it made of?
      5. What are the chief parts?
         a. Shape, size, material?
         b. Relationship to other parts?
         c. Assembly or attachment?
      6. How does it work? or How is it used?
   B. Process ("Technical" Description)
      1. What are the chief steps in the over-all process?
      2. What is done step by step?
      3. How is each step done?
      4. How is it related to other processes?
      5. Review the highlights.
II. Narrative
   A. Operation
      1. What's the over-all situation now?
      2. What was the situation?
      3. What has happened to change the situation?
         a. Cause?
         b. Effects?
         c. Examples?
      4. What did you do?
      5. Then what happened?
      6. What are your conclusions?
   B. Test or Research
      1. What did you do?
         a. Why did you do it *that* way?
         b. What was your objective?
      2. What material, equipment, and general procedure did you use?
         a. What factors were constant?
         b. What factors were variables?
      3. What did you do step by step?
      4. What happened?
      5. What are your concluisons?
III. Analysis

    A. By Classification
        1. What are the limits of your subject?
        2. What is your principle of classification?
        3. What distinguishes each class from the others?
        4. What distinctions are found within each class?
    B. By Breakdown
        1. How do you classify the components?
        2. How is each component broken down?
        3. How do basic parts differ within each component?
        4. How do basic parts relate to the whole idea, mechanism, situation, etc.?
IV. Recommendation
    A. Action
        1. State the problem or over-all situation.
        2. Describe the possible courses of action.
        3. Compare advantages and disadvantages.
        4. Draw conclusions.
        5. Offer recommendations
    B. Plan of Action
        1. Make general recommendations.
        2. Survey the problem or situation.
            a. Conditions.
            b. Needs.
            c. Developments.
        3. Explain details of recommended plan.
        4. Show how it can be implemented and when.
    C. Facilities, Equipment, etc.
        1. Offer a brief, thorough introduction covering:
            a. Object of purchase.
            b. Facilities selected.
            c. Reasons for selection.
            d. Estimate of cost.
        2. List standards for selection.
        3. Discuss advantages and disadvantages of other possibilities.
        4. Give detailed description of final selection.
        5. Summarize discussion with emphasis on advantages.

4. REPORT FORMATS

Report formats, or sequences, are commonly established by company policy, contract specification, tradition, and sometimes simple expediency. They differ remarkably from organization to organization and often differ within groups in a given organization. It is usual for large firms to require different formats for different types of reports. For example, the Detroit Edison Company made this distinction:

SHORT REPORTS	LONG REPORTS
Summary	Title Page
Detailed Results	Table of Contents
Discussion	Problem
Procedure	Conclusions
	Procedure
	Results
	Discussion

Other companies will distinguish between operations reports, test reports, planning reports, and status reports—and each will require a different format. Ordinarily the required formats will be contained in an official style book or operations manual.

Formats, as we discussed in Chapter 1, are chiefly for the reader's benefit, to enable him to find what he wants in a hurry. They differ in this respect from preliminary outlines which are for the writer's benefit. However, most writers feel that formats are substitutes for outlines and neglect the classification and analysis factors that outlines provide. As a result, they are disappointed to find that a format—far from being a help—is an obstacle to their thinking. Remember, then, that a format simply requires that you follow a given sequence. It does not tell you what or how to think.

A classification of format elements is given in Table III. The following is an analysis of each element and examples.

1. *Title Page.* The title, dates, and names which appear on the title page indicate the objective and scope of the report, the date of preparation and issue, and the author and origin. Title pages in business and industry are commonly prepared on printed forms. Title pages of short reports may also include abstracts. (See Figure 4.)

2. *Foreword.* Forewords are necessary only when specifically called for or when an author wishes to acknowledge assistance.

TABLE III. Format Elements

Element	Function	Contents
1. Title page	Identifies report	Title Author Authority or request Place Date
2. Foreword	Identifies report Gives administrative data — authority Acknowledges aid	Title Authority or request Series, if any Names helpers
3. Table of contents	Identifies topics covered in report	Title Main headings Chief subheads Appendixes Lists of figures and tables

4. Summary
  a. Abstract
  b. Summary
	a. Describes report
	b. Describes subject by para-
	  phrasing highlights
		a. Topics covered
		b. Summary of problem,
		  approach, results, con-
		  clusions

5. Introduction	Defines and explains report and subject	Purpose and limits of dis- cussion Historical background General make-up of report
6. Discussion ("Body" or "Text")	Narrates work and analyzes results	Procedure Results Analysis

7. Conclusion	Summarizes highlights of re-
	  sults and analysis
	May offer recommendations
		Paraphrase of discussion
		Detailed statement of how
		  results may be applied
		  — what should be done

8. a. Bibliography
  or
  b. References
	a. Lists sources in alphabetical order
	b. Lists sources in order of first mention in text
		Author — last name first
		Full title
		Place of publication
		Publisher (book)
		Date
		Volume and pages
		  (periodical)

9. Appendix	Gives supporting data too bulky or complicated for the text	Types of appendix material:
		  Complex description
		  Extensive data
		  Derivations
		  Sample forms

REDUCTION OF MERCAPTAN SULFUR IN
JP4 JET FUEL BLEND STOCK

by
Eric Simmons

for
Jolly Roger Petroleum, Inc.
June 15, 1961
Communication Research Co.

Figure 4. Title Page.

COMMUNICATION RESEARCH CO.
State College Driveway
Los Angeles 32

15 June 1961

Jolly Roger Petroleum, Inc.
MacAdam Road
Los Angeles 32

Gentlemen:

Attached is the report requested in your letter of
3 June 1960. The report covers laboratory results of
testing caustic treating, potassium treating, potassium
cresolate treating, and air caustic treating of JP4
blend stocks.

None of these processes would reduce the mercaptan
level to the 10 ppm required by Government specifications.
Preliminary studies, however, show that two other processes employing Bender and Metallic Lead may prove
satisfactory.

Very truly yours,

Eric Simmons
Chief, Technical Staff

Figure 5.   Letter of Transmittal.

They are intended to be strictly administrative rather than informative. Two examples of a foreword are:

This document, CV-1467, is submitted in accordance with contract letter 69-2 dated 3 June 1960, paragraph 4, item III A.

The assistance of Jeremey Harrison and Benjamin Taylor of the Adhesives Group is gratefully acknowledged for providing data pertinent to the conclusions of this report.

Information that in the past was included in a foreword is now frequently contained in a letter of transmittal accompanying the report. The letter of transmittal is a letter in every respect (headings, tone, salutation, etc.). It identifies the report, the subject, and the reason for the report. Unlike the foreword, however, the letter of transmittal also offers a brief summary or paraphrase of report highlights. (See Figure 5.)

3. *Table of Contents.* Reports of less than five pages usually do not need a contents page. Longer reports, however, require a table of contents with major headings and subheadings listed specifically. Avoid such headings as "Procedure," "Approach," and the like. (See Figure 6.)

4. *Summary Page.* Summary pages are often independent elements detached from the report for distribution separately, usually to a management-level audience more interested in recommendations than in details. Summaries of this type would therefore begin with a statement of recommendation or chief findings (as in Figure 7), followed by supporting discussion.

5. *Introduction.* The introduction provides background information helpful in understanding the report. Ordinarily this information includes definition of the subject (its scope and limits), discussion of the problem and what had been done previously to solve it, explanation of your general approach, and a forecast of how the report will handle the subject. (See Figure 8.)

6. *Discussion.* The discussion describes and explains what was done. It explains the steps of the solution with enough detail so that the work could be reproduced from information available in the report.

Standard procedures need not be explained as thoroughly as unusual procedures. Often, reference to specifications is enough.

REDUCTION OF MERCAPTAN SULFUR
IN JP4 JET FUEL BLEND STOCKS

TABLE OF CONTENTS

Figure 6.   Table of Contents.

REDUCTION OF MERCAPTAN SULFUR

IN JP4 JET FUEL BLEND STOCKS

SUMMARY

The Metallic Lead Sweetening process is recommended as a potential method for reducing mercaptan sulfur in JP4 jet fuel blend stocks.

Development of new jet engines has required parallel development of fuels of the JP4 type. Production of these fuels to US Government specifications is handicapped by lack of process for reducing total mercaptans to 10 ppm or less.

Five processes were therefore evaluated for adequate mercaptan reduction: (1) Caustic Treating; (2) Potassium Cresolate Treating; (3) Air Caustic Sweetening; (4) Bender Sweetening; and (5) Metallic Lead Sweetening. The caustic and Potassium Cresolate treatments were tested in batch-type treats. The other three methods were evaluated in small continuous pilot plant units.

The Bender and Metallic Lead processes were able to reduce mercaptan to specified levels. Since the Bender process incurs expense of royalties and catalyst preparation, the Metallic Lead process is recommended.

Figure 7. Summary.

REDUCTION OF MERCAPTAN SULFUR
IN JP4 JET FUEL BLEND STOCKS

INTRODUCTION

Development of new jet engines by the Army and Navy has opened a new market for jet fuels meeting U.S. Government JP4 specifications. Recent trial runs at the Oiltown refinery have shown that a profitable JP4 fuel can be manufactured there. However, this fuel fails to meet specifications covering the mercaptan sulfur (RSH) content and must be treated for removal of the mercaptans. Government specifications limit the RSH level to 10 ppm.

The removal of RSH is accomplished commercially by two general methods: extraction or conversion to a disulfide compound (RSSR). The extraction method removes RSH molecules from the fuel by contact with a chemical of high RSH solubility. The conversion method employs an oxidation-reduction reaction which converts RSH to a very stable and odorless disulfide. The degree of reduction in both methods depends on the temperature, strength of treating solution, contact time, and presence of a catalyst.

When treating jet fuel of this kind, processors have encountered side reactions which affect fuel properties other than RSH levels. Corrosiveness and smoke are most frequent. Untreated stocks, however, barely meet Government specifications.

Page 1

Figure 8.   Introduction and Discussion.

INTRODUCTION, continued

Before undertaking evaluation of processes for reducing mercaptans, COMMUNICATION RESEARCH CO. conducted an extensive literature search and also interviewed processors who have been working with JP4 fuels. On the basis of the information thus accumulated, the research program concentrated on the five processes most commonly acceptable in the industry. Laboratory investigation began on 3 October 1960 and the entire program was completed on 1 April 1961.

Complete details of procedure, results, and analysis are reported below for each of the four treatments tested.

CAUSTIC AND POTASSIUM CRESOLATE

Process Description

Alkalies remove the acidic mercaptan sulfur from petroleum by forming a water soluble salt. The degree of removal depends on a chemical equilibrium determined by type of mercaptan, type and strength of alkali, catalyst present, temperature, and contact time. In continuous refinery processing, the alkali is introduced downstream of a mixing chamber. After the mixing process, a settling tank is used to permit the treating solution to settle out by gravity. A standard wash in

Figure 8.   Introduction and Discussion (continued).

Other times, complete equipment lists and detailed steps are required, as usual, governed by laws of appropriateness.

Results and analysis of results are also integral parts of the discussion. They should be stated accurately and completely. Complex derivations should be placed in an appendix but summarized in the text. Generally, whatever stands in the way of clear continuity and narrative should be placed in an appendix. (See Figure 8.)

7. *Conclusion.* The conclusion summarizes results and your analysis of the results, and draws relevant conclusions from them. Recommendations should agree with the conclusions, which in turn must make sense in terms of the results and analysis. Thus conclusions must be based on data included or referenced in the report, and recommendations must be based on those conclusions. Furthermore, direct connections should be shown between the conclusions and the problem discussed in the introduction. Questions that might be answered could include: "Will it work?" "Should we use it?" "Can we?" "When?" "Who?" and "How much?" (See Figure 9.)

8. *Reference Page.* A reference or bibliography page provides a list of works cited or consulted and thus serves as a guide to further reading on the subject as well as an indication of sources. Consequently, references should be clear enough to enable the reader to obtain the book with a minimum of trouble. Forms of reference vary, but the form given in Figure 10 should serve for most purposes. On the reference page shown in Figure 10, the first item shows the correct form for a report, the second shows the form for an article, the third for a talk, and the fourth for a book. Note that if this were a sample bibliography page, authors would be listed alphabetically, whereas on the reference page they are listed in order of appearance in the report.

9. *Appendix Page.* Appendix pages may contain anything necessary to support your discussion. Ordinarily, however, they are used for long or complex tables, graphs, or derivations which would be included in the text if they did not interrupt the narrative. Sometimes sample forms are also included if they con-

CONCLUSIONS AND RECOMMENDATIONS

Of the five processes evaluated for reducing mercaptan sulfur content of JP4 blend stocks, only the Bender and Metallic Lead Sweetening processes were found suitable.

Caustic treating, potassium cresolate treating, and air caustic sweetening were found inadequate for use in batch-type treats. The Bender and metallic lead processes and also the air caustic sweetening process were tested in pilot plant units. Again the caustic sweetening process was unsatisfactory, but the other two methods reduced mercaptan to specified levels.

The Bender process, however, is covered by proprietary patents and incurs additional expense of royalties. Further, it requires extensive preparation of catalytic agents used to bring the process to optimum, and this also incurs additional costs. The metallic lead process, however, is readily available and performs equally well, and therefore is recommended.

Since the metallic lead process is already in use at the San Blippo refinery, technicians from Oiltown could profitably spend training periods there and then return to initiate metallic lead processing at the earliest possible date.

Figure 9.   Conclusions and Recommendations.

REFERENCES

1. Bobbin, R. H. "Mercaptan Content in JP4 Blend," <u>API</u>, Wilmington, Delaware, 3 June, 1960.

2. Peece, J. R. "JP4 Mercaptan Content Lowered," <u>Journal of Mercaptans</u>, XXI (August, 1940), 556-567.

3. Roleum, P. T. "Comparative Effects of Air Caustic and Cresolate Treatment," Second Annual AOPI Symposium, Denver, April, 1959.

4. Lousile, J. R. <u>Applied Analysis</u>. New York: Donker Publishing Company, 1956.

Figure 10. Reference Page.

APPENDIX B: QUALIFICATION-RELIABILITY
TESTS FOR FUEL SYSTEM
PRESSURE REGULATOR

1. This specification itemizes combined qualification and reliability testing for the fuel system regulator valve ZXQ56-5.
2. The regulator shall be operated while in the following combination of environments and while stable:
2.1 The operation cycle shall consist of discharge of nitrogen at 4 cfs from a bottle with volume about 1.5 cubic feet, and initial pressure of 4500 psi into the pressure port. Downstream volume shall be at least 3 cubic feet.
2.2 The temperature range shall be $-65°$ F. to $+165°$ F., in four approximate increments: $-65, +12, +90,$ and $+165.$ Input gas and regulator shall be at the same temperature within $5°$ F.
2.3 Altitude range for satisfactory operation is sea level to 55,000 feet. This is divided into four

Figure 11. Appendix Page.

103

tribute in any way to understanding how data was accumulated or interpreted. The sample page shown in Figure 11 contains test specifications that governed qualification of fuel system pressure regulators.

5. THE OVER-ALL DESIGN

Keep in mind that the purpose of an outline is to show you a structural plan of your report. In this respect an outline is like a road map. The dots and names on the map are not places. They simply represent the relationship of one place to another. Similarly, the headings on an outline are not ideas, but simply represent how one idea stands in relation to another or how one part stands in relation to other parts and to the whole. The same is true with respect to sequence of arrangement, whether prescribed or created: formats simply point the way by setting up guideposts. Neither outlines nor formats are substitutes for developing the ideas you have so artfully laid out.

As guides, however, outlines and formats are essential aids to thinking. When you first begin to plan your report you think in general terms. Then as you prepare your target statement and program plan you become more specific, and more specific still as you collect your materials. Preparing your outline allows you to see the whole project in perspective. By this time you have a clear idea of a beginning, a middle, and an end. More particularly, you should also have a good "feel" for the proper balance of structural and supporting elements your report will require. You will thus find the actual writing of ideas much easier because you have a good foundation and a solid framework upon which to develop them.

PRACTICE PROBLEMS: DESIGNING

1. A very familiar type of outline is a resumé of personal and professional facts usually submitted with a letter of application. Prepare a resumé of your own according to the following format. Be specific about dates, places, names and addresses.

Name	Address
	Telephone
Birth date	Birth place
Family status	Military status

Education

Technical Training

Industrial Experience

References

2. On the basis of your resumé, outline a brief biography of yourself as though written by someone else. Assume that this biography is to be submitted in support of a proposal to undertake a program in a field familiar to you. The biography might include:

> Name
> Present position
> Past experience related to the program
> General past experience
> Education
> Noteworthy accomplishments

3. Prepare an outline for a brief report on the advantages of joining an automobile club which offers the following services:

Emergency road service	Public safety programs in schools
National affiliation	Highway information in all
Insurance	weather
Recreational information	Weather information
Highway engineering plans	Lobbying in the legislature
Maps	Towing
Vehicle licensing and	Accommodation reservations
registration	Helping to keep gas taxes low
Bail bonds	New car financing
Touring service	Boat registration
Lawyers	

4. Facts about the consumption of coal, gas, and oil are listed at random below. Prepare an outline for a brief report describing trends in consumption of these resources.
   a. By 1975, energy requirements will be met as follows: coal, 33 percent; oil, 41 percent; gas, 24 percent; hydroelectric sources, 2 percent; atomic energy, some small percentage.

b. In 1950, gas supplied 18 percent of our total energy requirements as compared to 4 percent in 1920.

c. In Colorado, Utah, and Wyoming, enough oil is recoverable
from oil shale to last 135 years at our present rate of consumption.

d. Oil consumption in 1960 was 10,000,000 barrels per day; by
1975 it may be 27,000,000 barrels per day.

e. Coal once supplied 60 percent of our daily requirements for
energy, but now only supplies about 40 percent.

f. In 1950, the United States began to import oil in an amount
equal to 8.3 percent of present consumption.

g. A barrel of oil is equivalent in energy to 6000 cubic feet of gas;
when oil sells for $2.65 a barrel, equivalent energy in gas sells
for one-ninth as much.

h. Prices of petroleum products were 16 percent lower in 1950
than in 1925 despite a 24 percent rise in the price of crude
oil.

i. Petroleum can be transported much more cheaply than gas.

j. Reserves in oil shale could be made available at costs up to four
times the present cost of oil from wells.

5. Prepare an outline for a brief report recommending to high school
seniors a career with which you are familiar.

    I. What is the career or vocation?
      A. Duties?
      B. Advantages?
      C. Present opportunities?
   II. What education or training is needed?
      A. What kind?
      B. How much?
      C. Where obtainable?
      D. Any special licenses or exams?
  III. What qualifications are needed?
      A. Personality?
      B. Mental capability?
      C. Special talents or abilities?
      D. Physical limitations?
  IV. What is the financial outlook?
      A. Pay scales?
      B. Opportunities for advancement?
      C. Opportunities for branching out?
   V. How does one break into the field?

6. Listed below are facts and figures relating to world trade passing through the harbors of Los Angeles and neighboring Long Beach, California. Prepare outlines for separate reports intended for (1) top management and (2) staff management.

  a. The two ports represent 50 miles of developed water front.

  b. They are served by 115 steamship lines—a total of 5,521 ships entered the ports in 1959.

  c. More than 32,000,000 tons of cargo were handled in 1959.

  d. Principal imports in 1959 were as follows (rounded millions of dollars):

(1)	Automobiles and parts	126	(6) Coffee, tea, and cocoa	36
(2)	Petroleum and		(7) Paper products	34
	petroleum products	81	(8) Wood products	34
(3)	Steel mill products	56	(9) Meat products	24
(4)	Rubber products	39	(10) Fish products	20
(5)	Oil seeds, such as copra	36		

  e. Principal exports in 1959 (rounded millions of dollars):

(1)	Petroleum products	48	(7) Fruits, fresh and	
(2)	Raw cottton	29	frozen	15
(3)	Aircraft and parts	27	(8) Iron and steel scrap	14
(4)	Chemical products	24	(9) Construction machin-	
(5)	Industrial chemicals	24	ery and parts	12
(6)	Industrial machinery	20	(10) Animal parts—	
			inedible	10

  f. Principal sources of imports (rounded millions of dollars):

(1)	Japan	101	(6) France	21
(2)	United Kingdom	56	(7) Indonesia	19
(3)	West Germany	38	(8) Venezuela	15
(4)	Canada	31	(9) Italy	15
(5)	Philippines	21	(10) Belgium	10

  g. Principal sources of exports (rounded millions of dollars):

(1)	Japan	105	(6) Philippines	12
(2)	West Germany	24	(7) Venezuela	12
(3)	France	24	(8) Netherlands	12
(4)	Mexico	18	(9) Korea	8
(5)	United Kingdom	17	(10) Belgium	7

7. Prepare an outline for a report classifying multilateral treaty organizations existing in 1960:

  a. NATO (North Atlantic Treaty Organization) originated 4 April 1949. Greece and Turkey joined in 1952; Federal Republic of Germany joined in 1955.

b. SEATO (Southeast Asia Treaty Organization) consists of United States, Great Britain, France, Australia, New Zealand, Philippines, Pakistan, and Thailand.
c. SEATO does not have committed forces nor any form of allied command as in NATO, but rather a nucleus in which some limited military planning is carried on. SEATO is an organization of spirit and intent more than unification.
d. NATO is self-executing, which means that a country has to have agreement of its cotreaty members before collective action can be taken.
e. Canada, Italy, Belgium, Norway, Denmark, Sweden, Iceland, Luxembourg, Portugal, Netherlands, United States, Great Britain and France belong to NATO.
f. ANZUS Pact nations are United States, Australia, New Zealand.
g. ANZAM Pact nations are Great Britain, Australia, New Zealand, and Malaya.

8. Outline a memorandum justifying purchase of the refrigerating equipment described haphazardly below:

We need a 7 x 7 x 24-feet refrigerating facility.
Present equipment is incapable of precise control.
Present equipment cannot handle required sizes.
The facility should be capable of −100°F.
It would cost $120,000.
Subcontracting the work would be costly and time-consuming.
Facility lead-time (how long it would take to have the equipment delivered) would be fourteen months.
It would be used for part of the heat treat processing of precipitation-hardened stainless steel brazed panels.
There is not enough time under accelerated schedules to develop alternative processes.
The standard, acceptable process includes a quenching or cooling phase at −100°F., carefully controlled for selected times.
Brazed panels of the precipitation-hardened steels are required to meet design of tri-sonic vehicles.
The facility would be installed in the Experimental Shop.

9. From this news release outline a report narrating the Navy's experience with low bulk foods:

Ration-dense foods have been undergoing successful tests by the Navy to see whether they are acceptable and palatable as well as space-saving. Products specially processed to eliminate waste and bulk without sacrificing nutritional or taste values include: dehydrates, concentrates, precooked, precut, compressed and frozen foods. These have been found to be a promising solution to the problem of large yet not bulky food supplies required for extended cruising by nuclear-powered ships.

Since acceptability and palatability are subjective factors, tests are being conducted under actual sea conditions aboard ship. All items have been consistently received with enthusiasm, particularly prefried bacon, shrimp, and various cheeses. Typical menus include: baked beef patties Spanish style (canned hamburgers, dehydrated onions, canned bacon, and dry vinegar); apple pie à la mode (dehydrated apples, paste-type ice cream mix), and coffee (instant) with dry cream.

These foods were tested during the 43-day cruise of the nuclear powered USS Nautilus, served along with regular provisions. Both the crew and cooks rated the ration-dense foods highly acceptable. This acceptability justifies the supposition that ration-dense foods will become an integral part of Navy ration as soon as costs are lowered by intensified production and further development.

CHAPTER 5

Rough Drafting:
Introduction and Discussion

In the preceding chapter we talked about organization in terms of designing, breaking ideas down into component parts, building categories, and arranging materials to serve specific functions. Rough drafting is a third step in the process of getting organized. It is not usually considered a part of the organizing process, and yet it is the best means of clarifying the relationships of parts to other parts and the whole. An outline shows only what sort of things the parts are and what sequence they should follow. But you must also see how they actually work together in a system. For this reason, you have to work out or develop each of your parts in some detail, and show their interconnections as well. You will want to see how your ideas work together as well as how they go together. This is the function of a rough draft.

A rough draft is a personal thing. Nobody will read it (unless you ask them to), and you are in effect writing to yourself as well as for yourself. Thus you should not worry about matters of style or spelling or punctuation. You should be working out each part and linking it to other parts. To return to an earlier distinction, you should be erecting structural elements and supporting elements and assembling them into a working model. In the revision stage you can worry about problems of expression and professional polish. But now your chief concern should be to develop a model that can be evaluated for what it says rather than for how it says it. Relax and work systematically.

1. Do not try to write the entire draft in one sitting.
2. Start with your target statement in the form of a question.
3. Answer the question with structural statements composed from major headings in your outline. The result will be a summarizing introduction, giving you an over-all view of what you are going to say.
4. Discuss each statement in turn. If you have a good outline, each statement will form the topic sentence for a complete section or chapter, which can then be expanded by definition, description, examples, or analysis.
5. Work fast. Leave blanks for words that do not come readily to mind. Leave spaces for lengthy, complicated or detailed data that would be laborious to recopy. Leave room for later corrections or changes.
6. If you get tired or bored, take a break. Figure on a work span of forty-five minutes at first, and then expand it to your most efficient pace.
7. Try to finish a given segment at one sitting. A break in your train of thought might mean losing a good idea.
8. Above all, leave time in your schedule for putting your completed rough draft aside for at least a day before beginning to revise it. This will enable you to take a more critical view of it.

1. INTRODUCTION

The best way to begin a rough draft is with the introduction because this gives you a chance to indicate clearly what you will say in the rest of the report. Remember that the function of a rough draft is to let you see how your ideas fit together and work together. An introduction can thus give you a preview of coming attractions. Furthermore, an introduction can help to clarify your major ideas. Assume a double role, the role of writer and reader. Assume that your purpose now is to educate yourself. And when we talk about a reader in this chapter, we will mean you.

Begin your introduction with your target statement in the form of a question. Remember that the subject of your target statement is theoretically something your reader already knows something about. The predicate is supposed to tell him something about the subject. Since the reader's knowledge is theoretical only, the introduction should proceed by making sure that you and he are talking about the same thing. More than that, the introduction should also tell why you are talking about the subject at all. You will recall that in the planning stage you worked out a statement of objectives and purpose. Now this statement will come in handy.

Without a statement of purpose, an introduction is somewhat like those irritating people who do not know how to use a telephone properly. They answer the phone and say: "Hello." If you reply, "Hello," then they say, "Hello," again. This can go on for hours. But if a man answers by identifying himself and you reply by identifying yourself and the purpose of your call, then you can get right down to business. This is the function of report introductions. They set up the reader to receive your information and give him some idea of what he can expect.

Here are some general ideas to keep in mind when writing an Introduction:

a. Tell Your Reader What You Are Talking About

Avoid a long song-and-dance type of introduction. Begin with a clear statement of your over-all topic: what you are going to talk about and what you are not going to talk about. This provides a framework—and avoids keeping the reader in suspense.

1. *Define the situation.* What is the purpose of the report? What was the objective of the work?

This report presents results of . . .
   . . . a test program evaluating water-soluble glass as protective coating for titanium alloy undergoing heat treatment.

2. *Relate it to what is known.* What is the background?

Water-soluble glass has long been known and avoided by glassmakers, but its value to industrial processes is now being realized. Early in 1958 Robbin Steel Company evaluated about two hundred different coatings to protect titanium alloy in heat treatment. They discovered that with a binding agent, water-soluble glass in powder form may be held suspended in a liquid and sprayed on the titanium sheet.

3. *Relate it to the problem.* What was the problem? What had been done previously to solve it? Why was the present work undertaken?

When titanium sheet is heat treated in an air furnace at 1700°F., it is easily contaminated by gases in the air. This contamination causes scale and brittleness.
Aluminum silicone paint has long been used to prevent gas contamination. . . .
A literature search suggested the possibility of replacing the time-consuming and unreliable paint with ceramic protective coatings. . . .

4. *Relate your report to the situation.* What is the purpose of your report?

This report outlines the procedure which determined selection and application of water-soluble glass. . . .

b. Tell Your Reader What to Expect

Do not hesitate to tell what is important about your information. Remember, however, that most people will not be interested in all the details of your problem. A few people might be interested in all of them but the introduction is no place to get into them all. A rule of thumb in this respect is: *the length of the introduction and its quantity of technical explanation will vary proportionally with the technicality of the subject and its familiarity to the reader.* In general, the following suggestions should be adequate guides.

1. *Provide associations.* Try to show how what you are saying fits into what he already knows. The type of associations used will depend on how familiar your subject is to your reader. It is just as bad taste to insult your reader's intelligence by reminding him of something obvious, as it is to shoot over his head. For instance, you would not ordinarily explain the abbreviation IFF (Identification Friend or Foe) to a reader trained in modern aircraft electronics systems, nor would you stop to explain radar to a general audience. On the other hand, it would be perfectly appropriate to sneak in *brief* reminders in either

case just to make sure you are all talking about the same thing.

   a. Remind him—"It is well known that. . . ." "As you know. . . ."

   b. Re-emphasize—"This has been well known since Caesar's time."

   c. Recall—"As we have already seen. . . ."

   d. Use analogies—"This process is like wire stripping."

   e. Repeat—"This wire-stripping type of process. . . ."

   2. *Help him to understand.* You cannot tell a man something 100 percent new to him. He has to rearrange and relate it to what he already knows or it will not make sense. So after you have helped him to relate what you have told him to what he already knows, give him time to absorb it and show him how he can do so.

   a. Tell him what you are doing. Using paragraph headings, numerical headings, and other typographical aids is also helpful in this respect.

> First, consider the background of this problem . . .
> It is a matter of minor importance that . . .
> Last, but most important . . .
> There are three chief considerations . . .
> In simple mathematical terms . . .

   b. Tell him what you are not doing.

> Speaking now only about glycerine . . .
> Three-pronged forks are not considered here . . .
> Although abrasives are also important, they are outside the scope of this report . . .

   c. Tell him why you are including particular material.

> The following analysis will serve to show how automatic milking machines can lower operating costs.
> These figures seem to justify the complaints of the Underwriting Department and so should be considered here in some detail.

d. Tell him the connections between what you are saying and what you are going to say.

> In preceding discussions, some facts were presented about keolitic materials. Many of these materials have direct application in the operation of installed systems and will be discussed at length later in this report.
>
> Smog causes deterioration of rubber and therefore is an important factor in discussing the environmental conditions described below.
>
> The management philosophy just discussed underlies all areas of operation outlined in the following pages.

Here is an extended example of an introduction, reproduced from a report by Louis Maggi, "A Systematic Program for the Development of Ground Controlled Approach Systems" (Los Angeles: UCLA Engineering Extension, 1960).

The military services are faced with increasing air navigation and traffic control problems as a result of the tremendous increase in aircraft speeds and traffic density. Landing rates of 120 aircraft per hour under all conditions of inclement weather is the goal of military and civil aviation agencies. With the advent of TACAN, VOLSCAN, and other feeder systems, more attention must be given to the already crowded final approach (GCA) area.

The universal acceptance of ground controlled approach radar systems as standard equipment at all military and many civil airfields is based principally on the fact that no special airborne electronic equipment is required to obtain its services. A reasonable degree of pilot competence in instrument flying techniques and a functioning radio receiver are the only airborne requirements for a ground controlled final approach.

However, the presence of humans at two points in the control loop compounds the possibility of error or misjudgment. This factor has been a continual source of concern over the years, and various programs have been undertaken to reduce hazard through improvements in the radar equipment and in operator efficiency. But there is a limit to the improvements that can be expected to preserve or improve safety margins in GCA, especially with the introduction into general service of high-performance jet aircraft and large cargo carriers.

The CGA controller already has a full-time job analyzing his radar scope in three coordinates, and his job will become increasingly more difficult as air traffic congestion increases. Unfortunately, this three-coordinate data cannot be presented in a display from which the operator can merely read out position and command information. The operator's task is, then, exacting and fatiguing and requires superhuman precision. . . .

It is apparent, then, that GCA radars in the coming years must place more emphasis on the equipment, leaving the operator to act as safety monitor, ready to take over manual control when routine operations threaten to become emergencies. Each of the systems described in this report offers this feature.

Each of the systems has been designed for easy and economical installation in GCA radar centers. Each has been developed as an accessory that can be installed into existing equipment without major overhauls or replacement of units. Finally, each has been designed to supersede its predecessor by adding more capability to individual installations in whatever programs are dictated by requirements. The systems include:

    a. Automatic-Tracking GCA (Autotrack);
    b. Automatic-Voice GCA (Autovoice);
    c. Automatic GCA (AGCA).

2. DISCUSSION

In a rough draft, your discussion section can flow right on from the introduction. The discussion is, after all, an expansion or development of points raised in the introduction and consists of facts and figures translated into supporting narrative, description, or explanation. These facts may be necessary to support an opinion, explain a phenomenon, illustrate an obscure point, or explain other facts. They may be summarized statistics or facts showing which is "most" or "smallest" or "first" or "largest." But simply displaying the facts is not enough. They must be organized and arranged in clear, connected discourse in support of some structural point. Otherwise you would have nothing but a mass of unsupported opinion in the introduction and irrelevant details in the discussion.

In developing a rough draft of the discussion section you can follow a four-step process consisting of answering these questions:

1. What did you do?
2. How did you do it?
3. What happened?
4. What do the results mean?

Answering these questions, however, involves some artful handling of your facts. The four most common methods include:

1. Definition
2. Description
3. Illustration by Examples
4. Analysis

You will note that these methods parallel the four-step process outlined above, but there is no need to worry about keeping them parallel. The methods will naturally come to hand at appropriate times. Seldom are they the exclusive property of any step in the discussion process, but rather play a part in all of them. They are discussed in this sequence because you will find yourself using them accordingly as you compose your Discussion section.

a. Definition

Definition is the basis of discussion. People must be talking about the same thing in the same language in order to have easy communication. They must agree on what they are talking about, and this involves agreeing on such questions as what class of things the subject under discussion belongs to, what sort of things it includes, and how it differs from other sorts of things that seem to be like it. Such agreement is not always easy.

The problem is really based in the nature of our language itself. Words that point out or name things are readily understandable when the things are present. However, words also represent or symbolize things that are not present or that are abstract rather than concrete. When things are concrete and familiar, all it takes for common agreement on meaning is simple definition. But when things are unfamiliar and never really experienced, they are said to be abstractions and the words that represent them are said to be abstract words. The more abstract a word is, the more open to personal interpretation it is, and the more definition is required in order to carry on a conversation that does not result in an exchange of mere opinion, not to say an exchange of blows. Thus, *a man* is more abstract than *a man named Jones,* and less abstract than *man* (in the expression "Man is mortal."). *A man named Jones* is more abstract than *J. P. Jones,* which in turn is more abstract than *John Paul Jones. John Paul Jones* is more abstract than *John Paul Jones of Tusca, Alabama,* which is more abstract than *John Paul Jones, age 38, of 1962 Primrose Lane, Tusca, Alabama, Social Security Number 183147643.*

Fortunately for report writers this problem of nailing down meanings is somewhat lessened because of agreement among people in various fields to use words in particular and specific ways. The meaning of "pi" for example is universally established, and the meaning of words such as "aspirin" are standardized by law. Most professional groups have established nomenclature for particular fields, and it may be said that education for many professions is frequently, at least in part, a matter of learning their specialized language. Nevertheless, the problem of definition still remains because a report writer must use language commonly used by men other than specialists.

Many techniques of definition are available to you, separately and in combination. Perhaps the most common method is outright explanation by means of synonyms more familiar than the words being defined. Usually the synonym is put in apposition to, or next to, the obscure term. (In this last sentence, the phrase "or next to" is a synonym for "apposition.") You can also use antonyms, words having opposite meanings, and you can use examples to distinguish what you mean. You can also make outright comparisons or contrasts to differentiate between the parts of what you are talking about and something that seems like it. But in a report, the most common type of definition is what we call "operational" as opposed to "logical."

Logical definitions are concerned with the meanings of words. Operational definitions tell what a thing is by describing what sort of thing it is as a whole and in its parts, and how those parts are put together to achieve a purpose. We have already seen an outline for this kind of definition in Chapter 4, and we will discuss it further later on. In order to clear up our distinction, however, let us consider two examples. Here, for example, is an operational definition from the very popular Armed Services manual, *ABC's of Hand Tools:*

> Starting punches, sometimes called drifts, are made with a long, gentle taper which extends from the tip to the body of the punch. They are made that way to withstand heavy shock blows. This type of punch is used to knock out rivets after the heads have been cut off. It also is used to start driving out straight or tapered pins because it can withstand the heavy hammer blows required to break loose the pin and start it moving.

And for comparison this is the logical definition of "punch" from *Webster's New Collegiate Dictionary:*

> A tool, usually a short rod of steel, variously shaped at one end, either solid or hollow and sharp-edged, for various uses, as perforating, marking, centering, embossing, starting a bolt out of a hole, etc.; specif., such a tapering tool for driving the heads of nails below the surface.

Since many people would call a punch of this type a "nail set," you can see what kind of quibbling would result from using the dictionary's definition in a report without further definition.

For purposes of report writing, therefore, the following procedure is suggested:

1. Name it.	"A micrometer . . ."
2. Distinguish it.	
a. By classification	". . . is a measuring instrument . . ."
b. By analysis	". . . for precise determination of distances."
3. Describe it.	
a. What does it do?	"A micrometer measures precisely . . ."
b. How does it work?	". . . by means of a finely threaded screw of definite pitch, with a head graduated to show how much the screw has been moved in or out . . ."
c. How is it used? or What is it used for?	". . . to give fine measurements as small as 0.001 inch."
4. Give examples.	
a. Where is it used?	"Micrometers are used on telescopes or microscopes for measuring very small distances, angles, diameters, etc."

b. What is a typical use?   "Calipers used by machinists have mi-
crometer screws for making accurate
measurements."

Often a definition must be complex rather than simple, that
is, it must define more than one concept at a time. In spite of
its seeming complexity, however, the basic procedure described
above still provides the structure of a definition such as the
following:

Low drag boundary layer control (LD-BLC) is a method for reducing friction drag on aircraft in flight. The boundary layer is a very
thin stream of air that surrounds the aircraft. It lies directly on the
aircraft skin, and is formed by air that is slowed by the passage of the
aircraft surface. It flows much slower than the free stream velocity of
the air around it. This boundary layer flow is smooth, or laminar, at
its initiation and generates very little friction. As the flow progresses
backward along the surface, however, it becomes turbulent. The tur-
bulence causes large increases in air friction, which results in drag on
the airplane. (Friction drag should not be confused with the induced
drag associated with lift. Friction drag is "waste" drag. It contributes
nothing to flight.) By drawing part of the turbulent boundary layer
air through slots in the aircraft skin with a suction compressor and
exhausting it in the direction of thrust through the aft fuselage or
the nacelle tailpipes, a continuing smooth flow of air is obtained, and
friction drag is reduced. Reduction of friction drag brings large increases in endurance, range and payload for large, long-range aircraft.

b. Description

When discussing the function of his style, Joseph Conrad
said: "Above all, it is to make the reader *see*." This is the function of descriptive writing in reports no less than in novels, and
it is perhaps more important that the report reader see exactly
what you want him to see. In Chapter 4 we discussed how descriptive reports may be outlined, particularly the two common
varieties called "Machine Description" and "Process Description," and you have just seen how important description is in
the process of definition. But the problems we discussed when
talking about definition also affect description.

The nature of our language is such that a man will see what
he wants to see when we describe something to him, unless we

use exact descriptive terms. But are there such things as "exact descriptive terms?" Words like *hot* and *cold* are abstract and relative. It is not enough to define them in terms of measurement, for temperature may be measured on three different scales devised by Fahrenheit, Celsius, and Reaumur respectively. If words like *hot* and *cold* are evasive, what is to be said for words like *blonde* and *brunette*, *red* and *grey*, *bright* and *dark*, *fast* and *slow*, or *left* and *right?* Descriptive words of this kind mean very little unless you also provide some indication of time, place, circumstance, point of view, and standards of measurement involved in the observations they represent.

The basic problem in descriptive writing for reports, then, is to provide the reader with a description of the mental and physical environment in which an observation was made as well as with a description of the observation itself. In test reports, for example, this can be done by simply listing constants and variables. (See "Recording Data," page 49.) In discussion reports, it is done by explaining the procedure leading up to the observation. And in reports concerned chiefly with describing machines or facilities, as trip reports, you can of course fall back on the journalist's technique and talk about who, what, where, when, and how.

There are three basic methods for describing phenomena in such a way as to control abstract[1] descriptive terms. The most common and obvious method is to define precisely by means of actual measurement. Thus, when using the word *hot,* you would give the actual measurement plus the scale upon which the measurement was based. Another method is to give examples of what you mean by the term. If you want to say that an oven is hot, you can tell a housewife that it is hot enough to bake a cake. If you mean that a furnace is hot, you can tell a metallurgist that it is hot enough to heat-treat a particular kind of stainless steel. A third method of handling description is to use comparisons. When you are not sure of the exact temperature (or you do not want to commit yourself), you can always say that a particular day is hotter than a previous day. But, as you

---

[1] *Abstract* in this sense refers to terms representing the quality of a thing rather than the thing itself. A rose is a thing, but "redness" is a quality.

see, the further you move away from exact measurement, the closer you approach the level of abstraction where differences in personal feeling and experience make for wider ranges of interpretation.

These principles provide the basis for the following suggested procedure:

1. Define briefly.	"A blub is an ugly but harmless fish about 18 to 25 inches long."
2. Give a general view.	"Its head and body are much flattened, and there is a prominent fold of wrinkles along its sides."
3. Discuss details in some logical order.	"Its wide mouth has teeth in both jaws. Its eyes are small and beady. Its dorsal skin is slimy and deep, spotted brown. Its tail forks into three points, each trailing wisps of green hair about 25 inches long."
4. Analyze the parts.	"The blub has no gills but has small pores where gills should be. Its lungs are simple sacs. Its nine limbs (four anterior, five posterior) are finger-shaped. Its tail has a skeletal structure consisting of a network of spongy bones."
5. Summarize key features, bringing in comparisons.	"Unlike the grunch, the blub lives entirely under water even though it has no gills. Its nine limbs and strong tail enable it to swim very swiftly and . . ."

As with definitions, descriptions seldom appear in simple form. The following descriptive passage is from Dr. Donald B. Lawrence's "Glaciers and Vegetation in Southeastern Alaska," *American Scientist,* XLVI (1958), 116.

A carpet of mosses and litter six to twelve inches deep has formed; this is at first composed of a number of kinds of the ordinary forest mosses typical of the coastal forest. But, rather suddenly in specific spots and for reasons still unknown, a new kind, the bog moss, sphagnum, appears, paler and more yellowish green, at first in small circular patches, possibly where other mosses have been killed by fungi or by the urine of bear or wolf, and expanding from there across other mosses, shading them out as their discs enlarge. This unique genus of mosses of which there are about a score of species in North America and at least eight species in Southeastern Alaska, is so water absorbent that Indians after drying it on trees pack their papooses in it instead of using diapers.

c. Illustration by Examples

It should be obvious by this time that definition and description depend very strongly on proper selection and arrangement of examples. We said earlier that report writing in general consists of handling facts in support of some conclusion or judgment. These facts, as you see, commonly take the form of examples. Examples used in this way may be considered to represent "species" (sorts of things) or "specimens" (samples of some sort). But, for our purposes, we can make even finer distinctions.

Kinds of Examples

Examples may be classified according to what they are intended to illustrate. They may be used to illustrate characteristics of:

1. An entire system

    In all forms seen in this system, two features are the bowl and handle.

2. Instances reflecting a system

    In the demi-tasse spoon, teaspoon, soup spoon, and ladle—all the way up to the powershovel—the same principle is variously applied to move different quantities of different materials.

3. A specimen reflecting a system

    Except for its ornament, the teaspoon has the essential features of its family.

    a. Simple examples. A single, simple example is probably most common and is usually signaled by phrases like: "for example," "for instance," or "such as." For example: "All sales are checked by an officer such as the Comptroller."

    b. Typical examples. A typical example is one chosen because it illustrates a common (not necessarily average) characteristic. It is important to note that a typical example does not *prove* anything. It simply *illustrates*. For example: "In cases of doubt, a bill from Northstretch Electric, as a typical example, will be routed to the Electronics supervisor for acceptance and signature."

c. Composite examples. A composite example is constructed from characteristics of a whole series. We distinguish it here from typical examples because it is created rather than actual but, like typical examples, a composite example is illustrative only—it cannot be used for proof. Here, for instance, is a composite example of an engineering report summary page:

> A 72-gram brown Rhode Island Red country-fresh candled egg was secured and washed free of feathers, etc. Held between thumb and index finger, about three feet more or less from an electric fan (Grande Electric Model No. MCM-2404, Serial Number JC230230, non-oscillating, rotating on "high" speed at approximately 1052.23 ± 0.02 rpm), the egg was suspended on a string (pendulum) so it arrived at the fan with essentially zero velocity normal to the fan rotation plane. The product adhered strongly to the walls and ceiling and was difficult to recover. However, using putty knives a total of 13 grams was obtained and put in a skillet with 11.2 grams of hickory smoked Armour's old style bacon and heated over a low Bunsen flame for 7 min. 32 sec. What there was of it was excellent scrambled eggs.[2]

These types of examples are ordinarily so neatly integrated into common patterns that you seldom notice them. The most common patterns proceed from the familiar to the unfamiliar, the simple to the complex, or the general to the specific, and they follow rules of logical arrangement. Here, for example, is a paragraph discussing what is meant by a "driver salesman" under the Fair Labor Standards Act—the federal regulation that governs who does and who does not punch a time clock:[3]

GENERAL   A large group of employees known generally as "route salesmen," "distributor salesmen," or "driver salesmen,"

[2] DuPont Laboratory, "The D.P. Report," Savannah River, Ga., 1954, p. 8.

[3] "Driver Salesman," Section 541.505, *Defining the Terms...under the Fair Labor Standards Act of 1938*, Explanatory Bulletin, Title 29, part 541, p. 25. Incidentally, driver salesmen do not have to punch a time clock.

are commonly employed by distributors of carbonated
beverages and beer, cigars, and numerous dairy and other

TYPICAL　　food products. Typically, the driver salesman carries an
assortment of the articles he sells and calls on the same

INSTANCES　　customers at frequent and regular intervals. He confers
with customers, replenishes the customer's stock of goods
and if he is introducing new varieties or new lines, en-
deavors to persuade the customer to buy the new prod-

SPECIFIC　　ucts. He removes the empty bottles, cases, and other containers if these are to be returned to his employer and
delivers the articles sold to the customer.

Arrangement of Examples

The possible arrangements of examples are many. Some of
the more common arrangements have been discussed in the previous chapter with reference to the over-all structure of reports.
Now consider the most common arrangements of examples in
discussion: (1) in sequence of time; (2) by comparison and
contrast; (3) by cause and effect relationship; and (4) by classification.

1. *In sequence of time.* This is the standard pattern for narrative—first things first, then what happened next, and so on.
For example: "After repeated social drinking, the potential
problem drinker may begin to show signs of his future behavior.
Perhaps he will react a bit more violently to alcohol. Possibly
he will begin to show a pattern of making his drinks stronger
and stronger. He may then want just one more and begin to
drink in the morning and to drink more socially than ever he
had before. He is still a social drinker but the danger signs are
there."

2. *By comparison and contrast.* This pattern is commonly
used when the intent is to relate the strange or new to something
that is familiar. It uses examples that share similarities. When
the intent is to distinguish between two very similar items, it
uses examples that highlight differences.

Perhaps the most widely used form of *comparison* is analogy.
An analogy attempts to show how items being compared are
similar in many respects. A road map is an analogy, for it represents geographical relationships. A computer is often spoken

of as being analogous to the human mind, and so on. Analogies, in effect, are composite examples. They do not say that item *A* *is* item *B*. They say that *A* is *like B in some respects,* as in the following example:

The pupil of the eye has the same function as the lens of the camera, and the diaphragm of the camera is represented in the eye by the ability of the pupil to expand and contract according to the intensity of the light. The pupil admits the image and focuses it on the retina, just as the camera lens focuses the image on the film. The image reaches the retina and the film in the same, inverted, condition.

Obviously the human eye and the camera differ in many important respects also, but for purposes of *illustrating* the operation of the eye, the analogy is successful.

Arranging examples to highlight *contrasting* differences is common to discussion in classification and analysis, as in the following example:

The two labor bills differ on two major points. The House bill bars a union from putting pressure on employees of a neutral company to stop handling goods from a struck plant. The Senate bill, however, would also prevent the owner of a struck plant from putting pressure on a neutral employer to shut down operations. And where the House bill wants stronger restrictions on "blackmail" picketing, the Senate bill allows for picketing at any plant where 30 percent of the employees belong to a union on strike anywhere in the world.

3. *By cause and effect relationship.* This type of arrangement emphasizes "what happened because something else happened." It is very frequently used in analytical writing where the intent is to show connection between cause and effect. It depends very strongly on straight thinking and inference, matters to be discussed at length when we consider analyzing in the next chapter. For the moment, this example should serve to illustrate the most common arrangement—the problem is stated and then broken down into cause and effect:

A better receiving antenna system is necessary for picking up adequate telemetric data from satellite radio signals. The present signals are inadequate chiefly because the satellite's spinning and tumbling causes incorrect polarization of the airborne antenna to the ground antenna. When the axes of the airborne and ground antennas are not symmetrical, the received signal is split into three separate frequency components. Proper telemetric analysis requires that there be but one frequency.

4. *By classification.*   This type of arrangement usually features a breakdown of a given topic into main and subgroupings that grow increasingly more specific. This is the arrangement characteristic of most catalogues, manuals, and also textbooks. A typical example in brief form is as follows:

The simple saving of money on the water bill is not so important as preventing water from being wasted. For example, in this Company several thousand faucets are in use every day. Many of these develop leaks daily and frequently go unnoticed for several days before the trouble is reported. Many of these are also left dripping by careless users. Even a small leak can develop considerable waste if allowed to continue, and a carelessly left open faucet can waste even more. A check of a leaking faucet made last month showed that its slight dripping amounted to 90 gallons per day or 32,850 gallons per year. A similar check on a faucet left open carelessly disclosed waste to the amount of 97,836 gallons per year.

In the majority of reports, however, the standard pattern is to classify by enumeration—simply listing specimen examples, as in the following:

Activities of the Records Center for the month of July included the following:

Records received	32,733 cu. ft.
Records destroyed	12,547 cu. ft.
References serviced	30,639 each
Records refiled	76,882 each
Records interfiled	16,701 each
Filing maerials salvaged	$4,115.70
Waste paper sold	$2,429.18

By developing a records disposal schedule, the Center has destroyed nonrecord material and inactive records, and moved active records from expensive fireproof file cabinets to inexpensive cardboard cartons.

CHAPTER 6

Rough Drafting:
Analysis and Conclusion

1. ANALYSIS

Analysis is a process of demonstrating the parts of an idea, showing their relations to each other and to the whole, and showing how they work together as a system to make the whole idea what it is. The ground rules for this process have long been established as part of scientific method. They require that scientific ideas or conclusions:

1. Make sense, that is, be consistent with commonly accepted assumptions about the universe and the order of things.
2. Be based on facts rather than on opinion or prejudice.
3. Draw support from sufficient, valid evidence.
   a. Simple enumeration of evidence is insufficient.
   b. The greater the variation among samples or specimens, the larger the number of samples must be.
   c. Specimens must be observed under the following conditions:
      (1) At first hand.
      (2) By an unprejudiced observer.
      (3) By a trained observer.
      (4) Under controlled conditions.
   d. Support must be available from other areas of inquiry.

Ground rules for evaluating hypotheses (to be discussed later in this section) have also been established. Hypotheses must be:

1. Capable of explaining the facts under investigation.
2. Capable of being tested.
3. In line with previous, well-established hypotheses which might serve as alternative hypotheses or explanations.
4. Demanding of the fewest additional assumptions.

These ground rules will now be discussed in terms of deductive thinking, or logic; and inductive thinking, or inference.

a. Deductive Thinking

A report writer's ability to develop reliable judgments and conclusions depends on his ability to weigh and analyze his "facts"—his data, examples, evidence. When this evidence consists of facts that can be proven true or false, weighing them is a process of classification. Thus if all A's are found to be B's and all B's are found to be C's, then it follows that all A's are C's as well. This kind of thinking is "deductive" but is not to be confused with detective-type deduction which is "inference" and will be discussed later.

Deductive thinking follows the steps we have already discussed in earlier chapters when we talked about classification as an over-all structural plan and as a method for developing ideas. Now we consider it in its particular nature. Usually the process is represented in the form of a syllogism:

> All men are mortal.
> Socrates is a man.
> Therefore Socrates is mortal.

Syllogisms are man-made structures used as quick, easy tools for testing judgments. They are constructed according to certain rules of formal logic, summarized in simplified form below:

1. Syllogisms must consist of three, and only three, statements.
   a. A major premise naming and characterizing a larger class.
   b. A minor premise stating that an individual or smaller class is part of, or included in, a larger class.
   c. A conclusion, stating the relationship between the two classes.
2. Each of the three statements must contain two parts—a subject and a predicate—and each subject and predicate must be used twice in the syllogism. This means that only one subject and one predicate can appear in the conclusion—for example:

Major premise:	All men (S_1) are mortal (P_1)	$S_1 = P_1$
Minor premise:	Socrates (S_2) is a man (S_1)	$S_2 = S_1$
Conclusion:	Socrates (S_2) is mortal (P_1)	$S_2 = P_1$

3. A term must not change its meaning in the syllogism, as in these ridiculous examples:

1. Some dogs have fleas.		1. Men are mortal.
2. My dog has fleas.		2. Jane is not a man.
3. My dog is some dog!		3. Jane is not mortal.

4. Qualifications made in a premise must be retained in the conclusion. Thus, if a premise contains words like *all, none, some, many, few,* or *often,* the conclusion must retain the same idea if not the same words. For example:

1. Many redheads are hot-tempered.
2. Jack is a redhead.
3. Jack may or may not be hot-tempered.

5. A conclusion must not be identical with a premise. This would be double talk: "Black is white because black is white." A syllogism may have valid form but be meaningless because of a slick substitution of terms.

1. This rule is a money-saver.
2. Money-savers are economical.
3. This rule is economical.

An easy way of working with syllogisms is to go around in circles. You can represent each class by a circle and then see schematically whether one class is included in another class or not. Thus for the syllogism "Socrates is a man, and all men are mortal; therefore Socrates must be a man," you can draw circles like those on p. 131.

But now consider what happens with redheaded Jack and the statement about hot temper, "Many redheads are hot-tempered and Jack is a redhead, so Jack must be hot-tempered." Whether Jack is included in that part of the class of redheads who are hot-tempered is a question that cannot be decided from the syllogism.

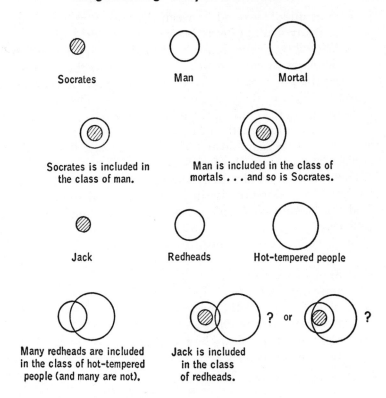

Socrates   Man   Mortal

Socrates is included in
the class of man.

Man is included in the class of
mortals . . . and so is Socrates.

Jack   Redheads   Hot-tempered people

Many redheads are included
in the class of hot-tempered
people (and many are not).

Jack is included
in the class
of redheads.

? or   ?

Alternative-type syllogisms use the expression "either . . . or"
and their major premises consist of two contradictory statements,
only one of which can be true. The minor premise then affirms
or denies one of those statements, and the conclusion affirms
or denies the other; for example, "You are either a good leader
or a bad leader. Since your record shows strong leadership, you
are probably not a bad leader." This kind of statement can be
very slippery. You must be sure that the alternatives you choose
for your major premise are truly opposite. In the statement,
"You either smoke cigarettes or you do not," there is no question. But consider this type of thing: "You're either a complete
abstainer from tobacco or you're a smoke fiend." There is a

tremendous middle ground between the two extremes—just as there are many shades of gray between black and white.

Conditional-type syllogisms use the expression "if . . . then" and their major premises say that *if* one part of the premise is true *then* the other part is also true. The minor premise then goes on to affirm or deny that one part is true. The conclusion affirms or denies the truth of the other part, as in this statement: "If wishes were horses, then beggars would ride. Since wishes are not horses, beggars do not ride." Obviously, if the minor premise denies the truth of either part of the major premise, the conclusion must also deny the truth of part of the major premise. The major premise in syllogisms of this type is often called the "condition," and the conclusion is called the "consequence."

The three forms of syllogism most common to reports are illustrated in Table IV. Seldom do they appear in so simplified a form as this. More often, the conclusion of one syllogism forms the premise of a succeeding syllogism and the conclusion of the second syllogism forms the premise of another, and so on. Or sometimes simply one premise and the conclusion are given and the second premise is left to the reader to supply. Then there is always the possibility that a syllogism may appear in perfectly "valid" form and yet be meaningless, as in this parody of a condition-type syllogism: "If the sun goes down in Des Moines and the tram tracks in Calcutta are slick, then the correlation between kitty-wampus and katty-wumpus varies with temperature. The sun does go down in Des Moines and the tram tracks in Calcutta are slick when it rains, so the correlation does vary with temperature." The point is—syllogisms are handy tools for building or checking judgments, but in themselves do not substitute for thinking. For all practical purposes, the best guide to deductive thinking is common sense.

Common sense supplies the premises of syllogisms. By common sense we usually mean a body of accepted assumptions about the world and the way things work. Thus the judgment that the sun will go down in Des Moines is an assumption no one will dispute, because we know from experience that it will and we cannot conceive of its not going down. If you accept the assumptions of the premises and the syllogism is in proper form then you must also accept the conclusion. Therefore, the real problem in building or checking deductive judgments is in accepting or rejecting the basic assumptions, a function of *inductive* reasoning.

TABLE IV.　Common Forms of Syllogisms

Form	Example	Description	Check
General	Vets are entitled to a bonus. Joe is a vet. Joe is entitled to a bonus.	Reasons from a generalization through a specific case to a conclusion.	Check the assumption. Does the specific case really fall under the generalization, i.e., is Joe really a vet?
Alternative	Vets enter either college or business. Joe is not in business. Joe must be in college.	A choice is made between two alternatives, one of which is affirmed and the other denied.	Are there other alternatives?
Conditional	If Joe is a vet he can vote. Joe is a vet. Joe can vote.	A condition is offered and also a consequence. If the condition is affirmed, the consequence follows.	The second premise must affirm the condition or deny the consequence.

b. Inductive Thinking

Our basic assumptions about the universe are products of our background, training, observation, and experience. Most of our thinking day (and psychologists estimate that day as consisting of only about 8 percent of any 24 hour period) is probably more devoted to working with these assumptions than to creating anything new, and eventually they become so ingrained that we never think of them at all but simply accept them as "common sense." We have seen how these common assumptions are the basis of syllogisms and thus of deductive thinking. Now consider how these assumptions themselves are acquired.

Deductive thinking is limited to things we know about or can prove to be true or false, acceptable or unacceptable. For handling things we do not know about—either because we can never accumulate enough examples for demonstrative proof or because other human limitations are imposed upon us—we rely on inductive thinking, variously called "inference," "imagination," "insight," as well as "common sense." Inductive thinking enables us to formulate generalizations and hypotheses.

Generalizations

Generalizations are *probable* conclusions derived from observable facts. They should not be confused with general statements which can be proven true or false, such as a statement like: "All the chairs in this room are brown." The kind of generalization we are concerned with states that all items of a class *probably* have some specific characteristics in common, since we have observed that many of the items have these characteristics. Again, it is a process of classification—looking for similarities and differences, then classifying them to formulate a general statement. But the emphasis here is on probability, and the resulting generalizations are, in effect, analogies. It is like saying: "The part is *like* the whole in many respects." And whenever a generalization is found to be proven true or false then it ceases to be a generalization and becomes a general statement of fact. There are two types of generalizations of this kind: uniform and statistical.

1. *Uniform generalizations* are concerned with whole classes. They lead from specific instances to conclusions about *all* members of the class or system, as in the statement: "When I eat green apples I get sick. Green apples must be bad for me." Obviously the larger the number of instances, the higher is the probability that the conclusion is reliable. But simple quantity is not enough to establish a valid generalization—quality is also important. Both quantity and quality are determined by the nature of the class under consideration. For example, if you were inspecting a carload of wheat, you could safely judge the whole load from samples picked at random in the front, middle, end, top, and bottom of the car. But if you were inspecting a carload of cherries, you would not only need more samples but you would have to take them from many more locations in order to get a good sampling.

2. *Statistical generalizations* differ from uniform generalizations in that they deal with *percentages* of a class rather than

with a class as a whole. That is, statistical generalizations state that the *percentage* found in some samples represents the percentage probably found in the class as a whole. This kind is very familiar in poll-taking: "Ninety percent of all steelworkers prefer air-conditioned mills." The test of a statistical generalization is again the quantity and quality of samples—the greater the number of *valid* samples, the more reliable the generalization will be. Thus no matter how many steel workers are interviewed, you could expect the results to differ depending on whether they worked near a hearth furnace or atop a skyscraper under construction.

Because your report is based on generalizations you are obligated to describe the conditions surrounding your work. You are saying: "My generalizations hold true for these conditions." And because your report will conclude with generalizations, you are obligated to provide thorough, valid samples in the form of data, examples, or other evidence to enable the reader to evaluate your generalizations for himself. When you are constructing generalizations, you are obligated to follow established ground rules and particularly to avoid jumping to conclusions—basing generalizations on too few data or on invalid samples.

Here is a check list for testing the *validity* of samples and data:

1. Is it *correct?* (Can you prove its accuracy?)
2. Is it *pertinent?* (Can you show the direct connection between fact and generalization?)
3. Is it *consistent?* (Can any exceptions be explained?)
4. Is it *objective?* (Are you sure that it's fact and not opinion?)
5. Is it *honest?* (Have you avoided half-truths or misleading statements?)
6. Is it *current?* (Is it really up-to-date?)
7. Is it *complete?* (Have you *all* the facts?)
8. Is it a *true picture?* (Is it typical or representative enough?)
9. Is it *verifiable?* (Could you do it again—if you had to?)
10. Is it *significant?* (Is it important enough to have meaning for the generalization at hand?)

Hypotheses

The process of analysis is based chiefly on formulating hypotheses or statements establishing cause and effect relationships. Hypotheses are formulated by means of choice. We choose from a wide range of alternatives: it could be this or that or the other and so forth. And we hope that all possibilities are covered before we make a choice. Naturally, the wider our range of alternatives to choose from, the better will be our chances of formulating the best hypothesis.

We start with a problem to be explained. (Why am I getting wet?) Then we seek all possibly relevant factors that may have some bearing on it. (The sky is dark with heavy clouds. The sidewalk is also getting wet. A drop of water falls on my head.) Finally, we put two and two together. (It must be raining.) You will note that we are still working with generalizations. (Whenever the sky is dark with heavy clouds it means rain.) But we also choose from particular factors. (There's a boy shooting a water pistol. A neighbor is watering his lawn.) We look into these other factors, investigate them for their connection with our problem. (That's not a water pistol, it's a Luger. The neighbor isn't watering his lawn; he's pulling crab grass.) And then after having established assumptions and examining all pertinent factors, we formulate our hypothesis. In everyday life all this happens in a split second. In scientific work it may take years and years. The process, however, is the same. Two traps are to be avoided now: (1) Do not call something an effect simply because it *follows* a cause ("Whenever atom bombs are tested, it rains in Milwaukee."). (2) Do not formulate a hypothesis that has no connection with the evidence.

Table V offers a comparison between generalizations and hypotheses, but there is a very common form of hypothesis that we have not discussed because it is a combination of both types of inductive reasoning. In essence it consists of comparison by analogy, as in the statement: "Both Oreville and Slagton have populations of 10,000, are county seats in Ohio, and industrial centers. Oreville has prospered under a city manager system, so Slagton should too." This statement asserts that things alike in some ways will be alike in other respects. In other words, it extrapolates from Oreville's experience to predict similar results for Slagton. This kind of reasoning requires evidence consisting of enough points in common that are relevant and verifiable

TABLE V. Comparison—Generalizations and Hypotheses

Type	Example	Description	Evidence	Check
Uniform generalization	Leaders inspire confidence. My boys are leaders. My boys inspire confidence.	Draws probable conclusions from specific instances and is concerned with *all* members of a class.	Enough valid instances to support a statement about an entire class.	Are there enough instances? Are they typical or representative enough? Can exceptions be explained?
Statistical generalization	Sixty-nine percent of the samples are brittle, so 69 percent of all this material must be brittle.	Asserts that what is true about the percentage tested or observed is also true of the percentage of the whole class.	As above.	As above.
Hypothesis	Production has fallen off because of normal vacations, plant repair jobs, and lack of orders.	Establishes connection between effect and probable causes.	Acceptable connections between cause and effect — verifiable and according to common sense.	Is cause sufficient without additional explanation? Are there other, more likely causes?

and also requires support from other areas of inquiry. Similarities should outweigh differences, and outstanding differences (such as the fact that Oreville's industry consists entirely of highly skilled trades and Slagton's of unskilled millwork) should be explained.

2. CONCLUSION

If the purpose of the introduction is to prepare the reader for what is to come, the purpose of the conclusion is to tell him he's had what has come and what to do with it. The function of the entire discussion is to provide a basis for analyzing what happened or what is happening. The function of the analysis is to provide a basis for the conclusion. And now the conclusion provides a basis for action or decision.

The introduction raised certain questions in the reader's mind. The discussion broke those questions down into parts and answered them one by one. The conclusion will now put them back together and show what they all add up to—a solution, an approach to a solution, or simply an acknowledgment that the problem continues to exist. The conclusion should *recall* the highlights and basis for judgment, *remind* your reader of your chief point, *apply* your findings, and *reassure* your reader that he has heard all you have to say.

The conclusion should leave no major questions unanswered. If you said in your introduction that you were going to treat Abel, Baker, and Charley, the reader will probably go to his grave wondering whatever happened to Charley if in the report you talk only about Abel and Baker. Further, the conclusion should demonstrate direct relation to the introduction and the discussion. It would be unfair, for example, if you brought Dog into the conclusion when you have talked only about Abel, Baker, and Charley—unless you can show that Dog is directly related. This does not mean, however, that you cannot point out the significance of your conclusions to a larger field than you have covered in the report. For instance, you could appropriately introduce some notion of the dangers to public

safety inherent in microwave transmission even though your
report has been concerned only with the theory or historical
background of transmission itself. But you must be sure that
all statements made in the conclusion follow directly from the
discussion—that they are relevant, pertinent, and significant;
that they are connected and consistent; and that they do not
contradict what you have said earlier.

1. *Summarize (recall)*.   The purpose of summarizing in the
conclusion (even though you may have already written independent summaries as you went along) is threefold:

   a. To remind the reader of your highlights:

   > As seen in the foregoing pages, the Laputa Laboratory is best
   > equipped and has the most versatile skills available for subsonic
   > aerodynamic testing.

   b. To offer the basis for your judgment:

   > The combination of the Inlet and Duct Test facilities with
   > their Wind Tunnel provides a rare convenience, supplying
   > complete internal and external aerodynamic data simultane-
   > ously.

   c. To recall how this judgment was reached:

   > No other laboratory visited in the course of six months of ex-
   > haustive field investigations demonstrated their potential for
   > speed and efficiency.

2. *Conclude (remind)*.   Your chief conclusion is worthy of
special treatment. Do not fall into the traps that beset so many
writers: they often get so involved in the development of details that their main point becomes obscured; or else the main
point has become so familiar to them that they think it is too
obvious to mention. In the rough draft, at any rate, restate your
main point. You may have stated it so often (in your target
statement, topic sentence, title, introduction, etc.) that you are
sick of it. But restate it in the conclusion if for no other reason
than it is standard practice in report writing. You need not,
after all, restate it in the same words—although this is recommended. Perhaps you can summarize it accurately and concisely

now that you and your reader are more familiar with it. Perhaps you can simplify it, inasmuch as you have worked out the details in your discussion. But by all means emphasize it so that it stands out boldly and the reader will not have to read between the lines. Instead of saying, "We do not have much hope that the Flimknapp model will work," be bold—"The Flimknapp model will not work."

3. *Recommend potential applications (apply).* Recommendations are the bread and butter of most reports. You will recall that reports are intended to be practical—useful for some specific purpose. It is up to you to tell the reader how your report can be most useful. Even when you report negative results, reports are useful because they will prevent someone else from running up the same dead-end alley. Do not be modest on this point. Every report represents one step in the progress of human knowledge. Even if hundreds of people have been over the road before, your report records a trip that you have made. You are unique and so your perceptions are valuable—either as corroborating what others have found or as denying what others have long affirmed without investigating. If you think this is ridiculous in the twentieth century, consider this: knowledge advances, not by finding the answers to the questions of preceding generations, but by finding that those questions were improperly asked.

Your recommendations might consist of nothing more than a suggestion that work be continued—or discontinued:

Because of the low thrust-weight ratios of magnetohydrodynamic power units, they are impractical for take-off. These units offer, however, a feasible method of propulsion for long-range space travel because they operate at low temperatures and produce specific impulses of over 3000 seconds. Therefore work in this field should be redirected and limited to long-range propulsion only.

Or they might consist of a detailed step-by-step procedure covering who is to do what, why, where, when, how, and how much money is to be spent. It is important in any event to remember that recommendations should be warranted by information included or referred to in the report—otherwise you give the reader no basis for assessing your judgment. Assume that your reader is from Missouri and wants to be *shown.*

Your recommendation also offers the final justification for your entire program of work. In a sense it is your report's excuse for being. Thus it ought to place your work in its proper light. The effect on the reader should be something like: "That man knows his stuff." This impression is best achieved by rounding off your recommendations to show how they relate to what is known in the field, e.g.:

Many other ways of utilizing nuclear energy for converting sea water are under investigation, but until one of them provides a superior system, the conventional approach described here can provide very attractive performance at a practical cost.

4. *Close with a final impressive statement (reassure).* The last words of your report should be those you wrote down as your target statement—modified, of course, by what you have learned since writing it. This is the message you intended to impress on the reader's mind. It should repeat, re-emphasize, and reassure him. It should not be a gimmick—such as you find in advertising copy ("Get some today and keep the bugs away."). Rather, it should be a statement that dispels any doubt in the reader's mind that he has been *told.*

It should be clear after discussing introduction, discussion, analysis, and conclusion that outlining and arranging ideas in sequence is one thing, but developing them in a purposeful, connected discourse is something else again. Because it is exhausting, as all real thinking is bound to be, many people think the rough draft is the end. But still more is needed, namely, review and revision. Your rough draft has enabled you to think through your ideas and has provided the basis for review and the raw material needed for revision. You could not do without this rough draft. Remember, however, to put the rough draft aside for as long a time as you can before revising. When you are too close to it, you know what you *meant* to say whether you said it or not.

PRACTICE PROBLEMS: ROUGH DRAFTING

1. Evaluate these brief introductions on the basis of what they tell you about their subjects and what they lead you to expect.

ULTIMATE STRENGTH DESIGN

Most current methods of structural design are based on the assumption that stress and strain are proportional. This assumption is far from the truth, especially for high strength concrete—and in particular, column designs. This behavior indicates that stresses and strains in concrete are proportional only at relative low stresses, but that at higher stresses the strain increases at a faster rate than the stress.

INDUCTION VS. RESISTANCE HEATING
OF STAINLESS STEEL

The field of power-reactor design and construction is expensive. Therefore more economical means of construction and operation of components are constantly being sought. Although many tests have been performed to improve efficiency of various components, the heating problems have thus far been neglected.

DEZINCIFICATION OF BRONZES IN
METROPOLITAN WATER SYSTEMS

Since October, 1954, metropolitan water systems have been reported as experiencing failures of valve stems. Examinations showed that the principal cause of failure was weakening of the stems by dezincification.

PERFORMANCE TEST OF A DOMESTIC
REFRIGERATOR UNIT

Refrigeration, in engineering practice, is a process of removing heat from an enclosed space which is to be maintained at a colder temperature than its surroundings. The present systems of mechanical refrigeration depend on the fundamental principle that some vapors or gases which do not ordinarily exist in the liquid state may be liquified upon being subjected to pressure.

DESIGN OF LOW-TURBULENCE
WIND TUNNELS

One of the most important tools of airplane design is the wind tunnel, a tool older than the airplane itself. The increasing complexity of the airplane design problem during the past twenty-five years has stimulated continued improvement of wind tunnels and wind tunnel techniques to provide data of increasing accuracy and applicability.

2. Evaluate the two pairs of contrasting definitions given below in terms of audience, purpose, selection and arrangement of details.

A. 1. A matrix is here considered to be an orderly and systematic array of similar components for converting one more or less complete set of variables to another more or less complete set of variables. Concern is with the logical structure of *diode* matrices, and particular interest is in the given number of diodes required for a given matrix. Practical design aspects, such as component and voltage values, time delays, signal attenuations, and reliability are not covered, though some practical applications will be considered.

2. A matrix is an ordered set of mn elements or constituents, a^{pq}, each occupying its proper place in the symbol, $\begin{smallmatrix} a^{11}\ a^{12}, \cdots \\ a^{21}, \cdots \end{smallmatrix}$ of the matrix, there being m rows with n elements in each row.

B. 1. A cow is a four-legged animal that gives milk.

2. The dairy cow is a mobile, animated machine housed in unprocessed leather. One end is equipped with a mower, grinder, and other standard equipment including bumpers, headlights, wingflaps, and foghorn. At the other end is a milk dispenser and insect repeller. Generally a conversion plant is centrally located, consisting of a combination storage and fermentation vat, three converters in series, and an intricate arrangement of conveyor tubes. This machine is also equipped with a central heating plant, pumping system, and air conditioning. It is available in various sizes, colors, and output capacity ranging from 1 to 20 tons of milk a year.

3. Evaluate the following discussion entitled simply "procedure."

In assembling a sweep generator from a kit the parts are all included. The equipment necessary for the construction is not extensive. The tools needed are screwdrivers, long-nose pliers, diagonal cutters, solder, and soldering iron. The diagrams are clear and present no problem in following them. The first step is to place the components on the chassis. The transformers, coils, capacitor, and potentiometers are installed. The next step is wiring together the components. The wires are made to run as short and direct as possible. If possible, the wires are run close to the chassis to prevent stray fields from forming. There are a couple of tests necessary on the completed instrument. Using an ohm-meter, the resistance pin 8 between tube 6-X-5 and ground should measure at least 20,000 ohms. The second test consists of rotating the horizontal phase control so that the instrument is turned "On." The tube AO2 shows a purple glow after 30 seconds. These tests showing satisfactory results leave only the alignment to be done for a completed test instrument.

4. Determine whether each of the following passages is intended to be predominantly definition, description, or analysis. Pay particular attention to selection and arrangement of details.

A. Modern requirements for structural reliability demand that fasteners be tightened accurately to prevent metal fatigue. The required accuracy can be achieved by means of a calibrated torque wrench. Since the torque wrench is a precision instrument it must be handled with care, checked for true calibration, and checked for accurate reading. When accessories are also required, necessary corrections must be made in wrench settings to compensate for them.

When a dial-reading torque wrench is used, it must be pre-loaded several times before any final adjustments are made. This will compensate for any free travel in the indicator. It is also important that the wrench chosen be of a size which allows 80 percent or less of the full-scale deflection necessary for a given job. This will prevent exceeding the full-scale deflection of the wrench and subsequent damage.

Torque should be applied with a smooth pull, building up to the specified torque uniformly—not with a series of jerks. The force should be applied at the wrench handle only, and the direction of pull should be at right angles to the handle. Torquing a nut already completely tightened with a conventional wrench will not yield an accurate torque-reading. Reliable torque-readings can be obtained when the final turn of the nut is made with a torque wrench. If, therefore, a nut has already been tightened with a conventional wrench, such as an open end wrench, it should be backed off and then torqued to its specific value.

B. To boil frozen lobster tails, place frozen tails in boiling water for 12 minutes, using one tablespoon of salt to each quart of water. To broil, thaw tails and remove bottom skin by cutting down each side on the bottom of the tail and peel the skin off. Cut the meat across the tail twice to prevent excessive curling while cooking. Place under broiler with meat exposed to flame for 8 to 12 minutes, or until meat turns white. If meat begins to shrink it is done. Do not overcook. For lobster thermador, use 2 boiled lobster tails, 3 sliced mushrooms, 1/4 cup Madeira or sherry, dash of paprika, 1/8 teaspoon mustard, 1 tablespoon minced parsley, 1 1/2 cups cream sauce, 2 tablespoons grated Parmesan cheese. Cut lobster into small pieces, cook mushrooms five minutes in butter. Add paprika, mustard, parsley, wine, and one cup of cream sauce. Mix well. Fill lobster shell with mixture. Cover with remaining sauce and sprinkle cheese. Bake in hot oven (450°) for 10 minutes. Serves two.

C. The AB/CDE-7PDQ high-speed digital computer is ideally suited to large-volume, continuous operation. It requires little maintenance and trained operators can readily adapt techniques used on other computers to this model. The AB/CDE-7PDQ operates on a power supply of 2 1/2 million watts and requires only 500 tons of air-conditioning equipment. This represents a savings of 20 percent compared with operating costs for its comparable competitors. Thus the AB/CDE-7PDQ can meet the company's requirements for complete semiautomatic processing at a cost the company can afford.

D. Sealing is the process of closing gaps, holes, or seams in aircraft structures to prevent the flow of gases or liquids from one area to another. Types of seals are varied and methods of application are also varied. But the principle of sealing is always the same: to stop leaks. Thus cabins are sealed for pressurization at high altitudes. Fuel tanks are sealed to contain fuel and fumes. Compartments are sealed from weather, acids, and corrosion. Surfaces are sealed for smoothness. And de-icing ducts are sealed to prevent loss of heated air.

E. Anyone who can make change in money should have no trouble in reading a six-inch scale. The decimal division is the same in both systems: $1.00 equals one dollar; $0.50 equals half a dollar; $0.25 equals a quarter, and so on—just as 1.00 equals one inch; 0.50 equals half an inch; 0.25 equals a quarter inch, and so on. Of course, when a measurement in hundredths is required and the scale is marked in fiftieths only, then the distance between markings can only be estimated for measurements in odd numbers.

5. Prepare a memorandum to Andrew Shultz, Director, Hydraulic Testing Laboratory, summarizing these findings and drawing whatever conclusions seem in order.

From January 4, 1953, to October 13, 1953, the Hydraulic Testing Laboratory handled 13,841 units of tubing. Of these units, 5,561 were given pressure tests. This amounts to a sampling of 40.1% for inspection purposes.

Only two errors were found on components under study. They were

DATE	NO. CHECKED	REJECTED	DISCREPANCY
1-3-53	41	1	Leak at sleeve
4-6-53	5	1	Leak at flare

All components are inspected four times before going to line stock bins or stock rooms. In no case was the tubing itself found to be in error by the time it reached the hydraulic test stand.

6. Evaluate the following generalizations.

A. Electric meters are one of the most accurate measuring devices. This is shown from results of 245 tests conducted in the Power and Light Department of this city, where the total average percentage of accuracy was 98.6.

B. Commuter business is one that everyone says is essential but nobody wants to pay for. In fact, it is not a business at all, but a public service. Since that is so, the public should subsidize it.

C. Propagation of television signals over a spherical, irregular surface such as the earth is affected by factors that vary geographically, including meteorology, terrain, and vegetation.

D. The lethargy of industry is nowhere better displayed than in the recent experience when 102 contractors were given the military and technical data on which to make a proposal on the technical approach each would use to develop a weapon system that would meet the requirements, but only 31 submitted firm proposals.

E. Because the industry is so close to the frontiers of science, the demand for experienced engineers to fill specialized niches will remain strong. Computers, digital data processing, airborne instrumentation, guidance systems, semiconductors, and microwave require high degrees of engineering excellence.

7. Evaluate the following conclusions.

A. Since it has been shown that small business does not obtain enough government business and does not know how to obtain contracts, the Committee recommends that regional small business representatives be appointed on a nonpay basis to correlate the major problems handicapping small manufacturers and present them with recommendations to the Small Business Administration in Washington.

B. A mere speed-up in production rates may seem like an undramatic method for stimulating new business. It is also difficult to apply because the Company would lose research and development time. But this loss would be made up later.

C. Three regional shopping centers will be opened during the next eighteen months, and these centers should attract customers from as far away as Inland and River Counties. The 15 million dollar Suburbside development will open in July; Moose Valley shopping center, with a 384,000-square foot department store, will open in October; and the Grossbill shopping center will open late in the fall.

D. Despite this extensive current activity, Greenhut is looking to the future of its labor force. Like the Paperpenn plant, it runs a training school where some forty apprentices receive comprehensive theoretical and practical instruction to fit them as skilled mechanics, electricians, toolmakers, or bench workers.

E. Let us take heart. An operational problem is a complete entity which working groups normally examine in full detail before drawing up a program. Thanks to vertical take-off-and-landing aircraft, giant air bases will soon be a thing of the past, and the improved air forces will be in a better position to fulfill their highly important missions, no matter what form a future war may take.

8. What conclusions can be drawn from the following information?

A. Commercial target-simulation equipment was inadequate to simulate the relative motion of a bomber in the air and a target on the ground. A Company-developed device has been developed which will do the job and eliminate the many costly flights necessary to check out equipment previously found faulty. In tests over the past six weeks, the device has shown high reliability when used with several bomb-navigation systems.

B. Weld quality in aluminum alloys is adversely affected by cleaning methods used to prepare the material for welding. Tests have been made on all aluminum alloys currently used for production, and all combinations of approved cleaning methods and welding processes. Specimens were then laboratory-tested. Cleaning and deoxidizing when followed by degreasing do not affect alloys *A, B,* and *C.*

C. A study was made of the anticipated funds that NATO and SEATO countries would spend in support of technical missions between 1959 and 1965. It was assumed that two competitive systems would be supplied under the military assistance program, freeing the budget for operational purposes. It was found that the same amount of funds would be sufficient to procure and support Mission *X* and Mission *Y.*

D. Of 4173 persons interviewed last week, 20 percent were unemployed; 30 percent had been unemployed in 1955; 40 percent had been unemployed in 1950; 60 percent had been unemployed in 1945; and 78 percent had been unemployed in 1940.

E. A cloud is composed of a great number of small water droplets, ice crystals, or both, which are separated from each other but limit visibility. The diameter of the water droplets ranges from 1 to 70 microns and averages about 12 microns. There are about 50 to 500 droplets in a cubic centimeter of cloudy air. Their rate of fall is so small that the slightest air current can keep them aloft.

9. Evaluate the following experimental program.

It was found that there is no correlation between children's television-viewing habits and their eyesight. The Clinic examined 496 consecutive patients attending for routine eye examinations. Patients were asked about the number of programs they watched each week and also the length of time television had been in the home. Television had been available here since 1951. Ages of children ranged from 7 to 18 years. For comparison, 816 children in local schools were asked the same questions. Eye examinations of both groups were correlated with viewing habits, and data showed no conclusive connection between viewing television and having eye trouble.

10. Write a rough draft of a letter to Oscar James, Chief GC/BAM, Pentagon, Washington, offering the services of Radex Corporation in the fields of systems engineering, computer programming, console design, display development, and photo interpretation. The following information may be helpful to you, but the letter should not exceed 250 words.

The organization and retrieval of large volumes of diverse information is rapidly becoming one of today's more serious problems. Major areas where the problem exists include business and industry, the military, the government, and the scientific and engineering community itself. In its simpler forms, the problem may involve, for instance, the automatic handling and analysis of business data such as payrolls, sales and manufacturing figures, insurance premiums, and other essentially statistical data. At the other extreme are certain complex military situations which require the concurrent interpretation, analysis, and integration on a very short-time scale of data from a wide variety of sources, including field reports, photographs, news reports, estimates of industrial activity, and the like. In many of these situations, there is the additional requirement to translate the information from a foreign language into English. The development in recent years of electronic data-handling equipment is now making possible the practical solution of many of these problems. Such equipment has the capability to perform arithmetical operations, make choices among alternatives, store and retrieve large quantities of information, and at high speed automatically perform long, complex sequences of operations. Radex Corporation is working on advanced information-handling systems characterized by large volume and widely different forms of information, short-time scales, and a variety of uses and users. Scope includes:

planning of systems and procedures, programming various types of data-handling equipment, and formulating requirements for new equipment. Research is under way on machine translation of foreign languages into English.

CHAPTER 7

Revising:
Sentences and Paragraphs

1. REVIEW AND REVISION

Review and revision consist of carefully examining a report's structure, development, and expression. They involve much more than checking for grammatical errors, spelling mistakes, and faults of punctuation. These are important, but even more important is a complete review of the over-all draft. Good writing is rarely achieved in a rough draft even by professional writers. They know that careful revision is the difference between a good, bad, and middling report.

It is best to delay your review as long as possible after writing the rough draft so that you can take a more objective view of it—as if it had been written by someone else who had asked you to edit it for him. Editing is much easier than writing. The report is on paper and you can approach it as a reader would. The memory of the sweat and tears that went into the work may be vivid, but if you follow some kind of routine editorial procedure you can always rationalize that you are working in a purely scientific atmosphere and that pride of authorship has nothing to do with the facts at hand. Conduct your examination in two phases: review structure and revise expression.

a. Review the Over-all Structure

Go through the entire report quickly. If you have not already done so, add headings or captions. These should be more than mere slap-dash notations; they should pull out the significant features of each section and major subsection. Also prepare your table of contents. Preparing the headings gives you a chance to check the logical development of ideas; preparing the table of contents gives you a chance to decide again whether the structural plan is the best—or whether there is still a better way. Then prepare your summary page, paraphrasing the introduction, discussion, and conclusion down to the barest minimum. And, finally, work back from the conclusion, checking for agreement with the introduction and with the material which supports points of emphasis.

Check List for Structure

1. Do main and subheadings in the table of contents follow prescribed or acceptable format?
2. Do they indicate appropriate balance and emphasis in number of pages devoted to each section and in extent of breakdown into subheadings?
3. Do they indicate logical movement of thought?
   a. Are there contradictions or inconsistencies?
   b. Have you omitted anything?
   c. Should anything be omitted now?
4. Does the summary page display a faithful review of what you were trying to do?
   a. Is the problem clearly defined?
   b. Is the general approach apparent?
   c. Are results and conclusions related to the problem?
5. Do the introduction and conclusion agree?
   a. Are the questions raised in the introduction answered in the conclusion?
   b. Are there direct connections between statements in the conclusion and data in the discussion?
   c. Are recommendations supported by discussion in the analysis section, reviewed in the conclusion section?

b. Revise the Expression

After a skimming review of the over-all structure and a closer examination of the development of ideas, reread once more with this question in mind: have you said what you meant and meant what you said? The remainder of this chapter is designed to help you answer that question. It will consider the elements that determine whether you communicate the ideas so laboriously accumulated and artfully arranged. In the rough-draft stage, you will recall, the reader became more and more important—but you were writing to yourself. In the revision stage, the reader becomes all-important. It is still possible, however, to think about problems of expression, from your point of view, as a function of accuracy, continuity, and appropriate language.

Check List for Expression

1. Is the meaning of every sentence immediately clear?
2. Do paragraphs move the thought along in smooth, easy flow?
3. Do words and word-order seem natural?

2. ACCURACY

The sentence is your best check on accuracy. Sentences depend on syntax (arrangement of words) and individual words to make meaning clear. In our language, the effects of variable syntax are familiar from the old parlor game in which the word *only* is shifted around: "Only I love you. I only love you. I love only you. I love you only." Or in such series as: "That is the blackest cat in town. In town that is the blackest cat. That cat is blackest in town. That cat is in the blackest town." As the number of words increases, naturally the number of possible combinations increases. Yet there is a normal word order expected by the modern reader that governs appropriateness of sentence structure. This order features the subject of the sentence first and the predicate following as soon as possible thereafter.

In earlier days it was fashionable to write what is called periodic sentences. These often started with their subject but the predicate or main verb might not come until the very end. The effect was to suspend complete meaning until the last word. Here is a familiar example of a periodic sentence: "When, in the course of human events, it becomes necessary for one people to dissolve the political bands which have connected them with another, and to assume among the powers of the earth the separate and equal station to which the Laws of Nations and of Nature's God entitle them, a decent respect to the opinions of mankind requires that they should declare the causes which impel them to the separation."

As a modern, "loose," sentence this would read: "People should declare the causes impelling them to seek separation when. . . ." The meaning of the sentence thus becomes clear quickly so that anyone reading fast or skimming can get the gist without having to read through the entire sentence and without the risk of getting lost or confused along the way.

The modern reader expects to find this basic subject-verb pattern, especially in reports. If he has taken a course in speed-reading, he has been trained to look for key words in key places, the subject first and then the main verb. He is trained to skim over modifiers or qualifiers, and will often ignore them completely. It is wise, therefore, to begin most of your sentences with their real subject and place the main verb as close to it as you can, saving qualifications and parenthetical remarks for later in the sentence or, when they are important enough, separate sentences of their own.

The secret of making an accurate statement is realizing the difference between real and grammatical subjects already pointed out in Chapter 2 when we discussed topic sentences. In a sentence like: "There are three lathes in Building 306, any one of which is capable of milling the new alloy," the *grammatical* subject seems to be "There," but the *real* subject is the three lathes. The real point of the statement is not that the lathes are in Building 306 but that they can mill the new alloy. It would be much more accurate (and easier) to say, "Any of the three lathes in Building 306 can mill the new alloy."

Beginning a statement with your subject also helps avoid

a style where modifiers and qualifications are so numerous that you cannot see the subject for the words:

> For a specified length mission, under prescribed maxima of environmental intensity, applied concurrently in a laboratory (simulated environments) test somewhat similar to "hot" qualification-approval life tests for completed valves, it is proposed that a number (tentatively set at 10 percent of the valves proposed and produced in addition to those produced as "spares") of simulated operation use endurance tests be performed. . . .

This kind of writing usually results when a writer writes as he is thinking. It is acceptable for a rough draft but it requires straightening out in revision. This is easily done by pinpointing the subject thus:

> Simulated operational endurance tests are proposed for 10 percent of the valves (tentatively) apart from those produced as "spares." The tests shall be for a mission of specified length, conducted under environmental intensities that follow prescribed maxima. These intensities shall be applied concurrently in a laboratory test involving simulated environments. The entire test program would thus be similar to "hot" life tests for approval and qualification of completed valves.

Sometimes you will want to vary sentence structure for the sake of avoiding monotony (as we will discuss later), but in a report you would do well to think about subjects and main verbs as structural elements and all other words, phrases, and clauses as supporting elements subordinate to them. The structural elements should be kept up front.

Careful attention must be paid to many points of style to ensure accuracy of expression. The following check list may serve as a useful guide.

Check List for Accuracy

1. Do sentences begin with their real subjects?
2. Have you said what you mean?
   a. Have you put your emphasis where it belongs? Which did you mean?

This tool is one we can afford, if I understand you.
If I understand you, this tool is one we can afford.
This tool, if I understand you, is one we can afford.
We can afford, if I understand you, this tool.
We can, if I understand you, afford this tool.

b. Have you put the most important ideas in short sentences? Which did you mean?

> The new man is from Ohio and is an impressive engineer and works hard.
>
> The new man from Ohio is an impressive engineer. He works hard.
>
> The new man from Ohio is a hard worker. He is also an impressive engineer.

c. Have you arranged ideas in order of ascending importance? Or does it look like this?

> We salute three great Americans—Washington, Lincoln, and Robert Hall.

d. Have you put equally emphatic or similar ideas in balanced, or parallel, construction? When two or more words or ideas are parallel in meaning they should be parallel in form.

> *Not:* This proposal like many others, has several good and also bad features. The Technical Plan is better than the Management Plan which is weak.
>
> *But:* This proposal is in some respects good; in other respects bad. The Technical Plan is strong; the Management Plan weak.

3. Have you made sense?
   a. Have you avoided needless introductory and confusing words?

   > *Not:* It is expected that with further study there is a good chance that the design may be improved.
   >
   > *But:* The design may be improved with further study.

   b. Have you avoided dangling modifiers?

Not: When packed in metal containers, the shipper can save 40 percent.

But: When the material is packed in metal containers, the shipper can save 40 percent.

c. Have you avoided unnecessary shifts in subject and verb?

Not: First we will list specimens, then statistical ranking will be prepared.

But: First we will list specimens, then prepare statistical ranking.

d. Have you avoided shifting the meaning of a word used more than once in the same statement?

Not: The result of this test was the following result:
But: This test resulted in the following:

e. Have you avoided inexact references?

Not: The racks were sold to a customer rusting in the yard.
But: The racks rusting in the yard were sold to a customer.

f. Have you avoided confusing punctuation?

Not: After the invoice is prepared, by the comptometer clerk a check is prepared.

But: After the invoice is prepared, by the clerk of course, a check is prepared.

g. Have you avoided double meaning?

Not: A carton of 90-proof alcohol disappeared and security personnel are working on the case.

But: Security personnel are investigating the disappearance of a carton of 90-proof alcohol.

h. Have you avoided illogical comparisons?

Not: This process is cheaper than Johnson.
But: This process is cheaper than Johnson's.

i. Have you avoided incomplete comparisons?

Not: This solution is milder.
But: This solution is milder than lye.

j. Have you avoided nonsense?

Not: Parts will be stored in the old warehouse while the new warehouse is being constructed from materials of the old one.

But: Parts will be stored in the old warehouse, then transferred, because the old warehouse is to be torn down and its materials salvaged for construction of the new one.

4. Have you kept it short?
   a. Have you used the basic pattern of subject followed by verb?

   Not: Increases in sales of 10 percent were obtained in June.
   But: Sales increased 10 percent in June.

   b. Have you kept subject and verb close together?

   Not: Alloy specimens which were bare, coated, and lubricated were formed in a power-brake press using a punch and die that produced galling on the bare alloy.
   But: Alloy specimens in three conditions—bare, coated, and lubricated—were formed on a power-brake press. The press used a punch and die that produced galling on the bare alloy.

   c. Have you changed unnecessarily long clauses to phrases?

   Not: Cutting tubes that will have no burrs has posed a problem for manufacturers.
   But: Cutting tubes without burrs has posed a problem for manufacturers.

   d. Have you shortened unnecessarily long phrases?

   Not: It is difficult to cut tubing without burring it.
   But: Cutting tubes without burrs is difficult.

   e. Have you used specific facts and figures?

   Not: a considerable period, in the neighborhood of six
   But: six months (or six years), 5.5

5. Have you cut out excess verbiage?
   a. Introductory expressions that serve no purpose.

   there is . . ., it is . . ., thus it is seen that . . .

b. Unnecessary words.

>needless words that may be present (needless words)
>at a distance of 100 feet (at 100 feet)
>proved to be of unsatisfactory nature (proved to be
>   unsatisfactory)
>remember the fact that (remember that)
>6 P.M. in the evening (6 P.M.)
>until such time as it can be shown (until it can be shown)

c. Beating about the bush.

>in the majority of cases, on a few occasions, in a number of
>   instances

6. Have you chosen the right word?
  a. Have you considered connotation as well as denotation?
     Consider the suggestions carried by these synonyms:

>potency, puissance, strength, energy, force, power
>examination, inquiry, scrutiny, investigation
>transparent, translucent, lucid, diaphanous
>moved, prompted, impelled, instigated, actuated
>price, value, charge, cost, expense, worth
>walk, trudge, plod, wander, prowl

  b. Have you chosen the right nouns?
    (1) Some simply point out: belt, machine, tool
    (2) Some involve comparisons: garment—clothes, home
        —house

  c. Have you used verbs that stress doing?

>*Not:* No action was taken by the Investigating Board.
>*But:* The Investigating Board took no action.

  d. Have you used exact verbs?

>*Not:* The bracket is held by six bolts.
>*But:* Six bolts fasten the bracket.

  e. Have you chosen the right adverbs and adjectives?
    (1) Some combine qualities with actions: softly, heavily,
        clumsily (adverbs); soft, heavy, clumsy (adjectives)
    (2) Some emphasize: solidly, efficiently, successfully

3. CONTINUITY

While accuracy helps you say what you mean, continuity helps to insure that you mean what you say. For when you straighten out the progression of your ideas, you put them into their proper perspective. Suppose, for example, that you are faced with this paragraph[1] in your rough draft:

New data-gathering and reduction techniques are becoming necessary to solve the complex instrumentation problems associated with the design and testing of high speed aircraft. Many of these problems arise from present-day emphasis on the empirical techniques as a major design tool in the development of new aircraft. The quantity and accuracy of physical measurements required by this technique have increased tremendously during the past few years.

You realize that something is wrong here, but just cannot put your finger on it. So you break it down into its basic ideas:

New data techniques are necessary. They are necessary to solve instrumentation problems. Instrumentation problems are accentuated by emphasis on empirical techniques. Empirical techniques require more physical measurements and more accurate ones than previously.

And now you realize that the sequence is out of line, so you rearrange it:

Emphasis on empirical techniques accentuates instrumentation problems. Empirical techniques require more physical measurements with greater accuracy than ever before. Therefore new data techniques are necessary for solving problems in instrumentation.

Finally, having straightened out the relationships among the parts of the general idea, you can now make them work together. You can make them display their proper relationships by combining similar parts and separating dissimilar parts, thus:

Because empirical techniques are emphasized as major design tools in developing new aircraft today, many problems connected with in-

[1] The examples are modeled after those used by Thurston Griggs in a talk at the Convention of the Institute of Radio Engineers in New York, March, 1958.

strumentation are becoming serious. Since empirical techniques require it, physical measurements have increased tremendously during
the past few years in accuracy and in quantity. It is therefore becoming necessary to find new techniques for gathering and processing
data, so that complex problems of instrumentation associated with
the design and testing of high-speed aircraft can be solved.

You may have noticed that in establishing the proper relationships, we made some parts of the idea less important than
other parts. Subordination is achieved by using such words as
"because," "since," and "so that." Other devices may be used
as well, as we saw in the Accuracy Checklist. The desired effect
of subordination is not only to show relationships but also to
help achieve continuity smoothly and easily.

How is continuity achieved? The paragraph is the best starting place. As a "mental mouthful," a paragraph should carry
only so much meaning as the mind can chew, swallow, and digest
at one reading. It is obvious that a paragraph carrying only one
idea will be more digestible than a paragraph packed like a sar-
dine can. At the other extreme, a paragraph with no substantial
ideas is simply verbiage. Of course, every paragraph cannot be
pared down to only the essential idea. Some elucidation is necessary, not only to clarify meaning but to make reading easier.
Thus some paragraphs may consist of nothing more than an explanation of what is to come, or a reminder that you have finished developing one idea and will now turn to another.
Paragraphs of this type are called transitional and are essential
in long reports. A long paragraph may be broken into smaller
ones but at the risk of overemphasizing a minor point and losing
the major idea. On the other hand, a short paragraph of one
sentence is seldom justified—on the assumption that any idea
worth mentioning is worth developing or discussing.

For the most part, however, paragraphs are logical functional
units: they state ideas and develop them in familiar structural
patterns discussed in previous chapters. In terms of the structure-plus-support distinction we have talked about before, paragraphs commonly begin with a structural statement, the topic
sentence or generalization to be developed in the paragraph.
The structural statement is followed by substructural sentences
which qualify or explain its terms and by supporting sentences

consisting of (1) repetition in the same words, (2) restatement in other words, (3) general illustration, (4) specific illustration, (5) explanation or corroboration from authorities. Here are some examples of supporting techniques:

REPETITION

Besides thorough engineering know-how and integrity, another requirement for the professional engineer is *reputation*. As an engineer goes through life, he is constantly building his reputation. He can build a good reputation or a bad reputation. It depends entirely on the manner in which he deals with his fellow men. If he does good engineering work, if he is honest and fair, if he works hard at his tasks, if he is tolerant and upholds his profession with dignity and honor—avoiding association with enterprises of questionable character—he will build an excellent reputation. Without a good reputation, he will not advance in engineering.

RESTATEMENT

In the past forty years the demand for engineers spread into certain types of operations and management because of the rising technical complexity of services and products. Decisions had to be made by people who understood the technical implications of such decisions. It was recently reported that nearly half of the top three men in the 800 major manufacturing firms of the nation had been trained as engineers. Forty years ago most of these positions were held by accountants, lawyers, financiers, and self-made production men.

GENERAL ILLUSTRATION

In metal bonding, cure cycles are applied by sealing the assembly within a flexible diaphragm and subjecting the sealed unit to heat and pressure in an autoclave. Diaphragms used in the process deteriorate rapidly at the elevated temperatures required for metal bonding in air heated autoclaves. Diaphragms made of high quality elastomer-coated fabrics, widely used in the industry, are often used for this purpose.

SPECIFIC ILLUSTRATION

Two dash numbers must be used when ordering these optical targets; for example, OT2500-194-17. The first dash number (194) designates a target with a circle pattern, and the second dash number (17) designates the size of circle and type of lens. A chart is available to assist in ordering the exact target with circle pattern. The dash number in the left hand column represents the second dash number to be used when ordering. It must always be preceded by OT2500-194.

CORROBORATION

Throughout the nation, facilities are inadequate for prevention and treatment of a predelinquent or delinquent child. According to statistics compiled by Arthur V. Jones, one of every two cities with over 10,000 population in the United States has no special juvenile police officer; five out of ten counties have no juvenile probation services; six out of ten juvenile probation officers have no training in social work; three out of ten state training schools have no staff social workers; and four out of ten have no staff psychologists. In the light of figures presented in this report, plus Dr. Jones's statistics, our inadequacies are shocking.

The structure-plus-support pattern distinguishes a well-developed paragraph from the staccato, jerking primer-style paragraph such as the following sample:

The period of transition has not entirely passed. Normal human resistance to change is being overcome. Personnel are gaining a working knowledge of the advantages in the reorganization. Efficiency is increasing proportionately with proficiency in using new systems. The period of transition will soon be over.

The trouble with this paragraph is that it consists of structural sentences entirely, without any support. By adding supporting statements it can be given substance as well as continuity:

The period of transition has not entirely passed, for there are still groups in the organization who find working together awkward and uncongenial. Some of the key people in each group have submitted resignations and have been scheduled for interviews with the Personnel Department. Generally, however, this normal resistance to change is being overcome as the people experience the advantages of working with people from other groups. They have exchanged improved techniques in performing joint work and have shared ideas from their collective past experiences. Efficiency is thus increasing proportionately with people's proficiency in using new systems which are found to be better than other systems. With the assistance of the

Personnel Department and the increasing experience of the men themselves, the period of transition will soon be over.

You might find it interesting to look for the original wording in the revised paragraph. You will see that the additions consist of (1) answering questions such as who, what, why, how, where, and when, and (2) using transitional devices to tie the narrative together. Transitions are the connecting links between one point and another. A simple mechanical device is the use of headings, but headings alone are seldom vital enough to show shifts in thoughts. Words, phrases, sentences, even whole paragraphs are often required to indicate logical relationships, mark shifts in subject, tell the reader what is to come, and remind him of what is being done.

The following check list is designed to help you use techniques to maintain continuity.

Check List for Continuity

This sample paragraph shows how continuity is achieved [1]. It is achieved by means of devices listed below, which are really matters of common sense. The more they [2] are used, the more familiar they become to a writer. They are already unconsciously familiar to readers because most good writing features natural continuity. We get so used to it that we hardly notice it. But we notice when it is missing, because a paragraph seems unnatural without it. Thus [3] you can check continuity by having someone read your work aloud to you and hearing for yourself whether it sounds natural [4].

1. Have you used a deductive order?
    Going from general to specific: giving the over-all picture and then filling in the details?
2. Have you used echoes?
    Repeating words from statement to statement, or using words (synonyms or pronouns) to echo the subject of preceding or following statements?
3. Have you used connecting words?
    Showing relations between statements by means of words like "thus," "however," "finally"?
4. Have you combined related ideas?
    Making one of the ideas a phrase or clause, or using a common subject or verb for parallel ideas.

5. Have you constructed paragraphs on this basic pattern?
   a. Topic sentence stating the subject and something about it.
   b. Discussion of the topic sentence.
   c. Conclusion connecting the topic sentence and the discussion.

TOPIC SENTENCE   The world's earliest technical document is a clay tablet excavated in Iraqu in 1950.[2] Inscribed
DISCUSSION   about 1700 B.C., according to Dr. Samuel Kramer of the University of Pennsylvania, it contains about 35 lines of heiroglyphics. Eight other tablets found on the same spot combine with it to form a 109-line document consisting of a farmer's instructions to his son. It includes such detailed instructions as how to grow a successful crop by means of irrigation, how to prepare tools, how to sow, and how to plow. It also includes such specific instructions as: "Keep an eye on the man who puts barley seed in the ground and make sure he spaces it two fingers uniformly." The document is filled with technical information about watering, recognizing diseases, harvesting, and winnowing, and concludes with exact prayers to be chanted before each
CONCLUSION   operation. The Foreword, in fact, which appears at the end, acknowledges that the rules of farming were laid down by the god Ninurta who was perhaps the world's first technical writer.

6. Have you limited your paragraphs to ideas that can be developed within their bounds?
   Check the construction of the paragraph below by tracing a pencil line from the subject of the topic sentence to the subjects of other sentences in the paragraph. If there is substantially direct connection then the paragraph is probably well unified.

   A paragraph is a miniature report within a report, but it does not stand alone doing nothing. It is one unit of thought, integral and essential. It serves to carry the report one step

[2] See Samuel Kramer, *History Begins at Sumar*, New York, Doubleday Anchor, 1959, pp. 65-69.

along, or to expand on some point raised in a previous paragraph, or to make a transition from one idea to another. A paragraph's versatility is limited only by the imagination of the writer, and its flexibility allows for narrative, description, classification, and enumeration. A paragraph is thus a fundamental building block in any type of writing.

7. Have you made smooth transitions?
   a. Have you used headings?
   b. Have you used words, phrases, sentences, or whole paragraphs to:
      (1) Indicate logical relationships: "On the other hand. . . ."
      (2) Tell a reader what is coming: "Now let us turn to. . . ."
      (3) Remind the reader of what he has read: "As we have seen. . . ."
      (4) Signal a shift in subject: "In addition to this. . . ."
      (5) Remind the reader of what you are doing: "We are discussing rutabagas not spinach. . . ."
8. Have you used guideposts—connecting words?

GUIDEPOSTS	TO SHOW
also	addition
and	addition
besides	addition
but	exception
consequently	cause-effect
first	time
furthermore	addition
however	exception
moreover	addition
nevertheless	exception
still	exception
then	time, cause-effect
therefore	cause-effect
thus	cause-effect
yet	exception

9. Have you varied sentence structure?
   Here are some possible ways of varying sentence structure

and thus avoiding "primer" style while improving continuity:

a. Use conditional statements: "If the equipment is lubricated, it will operate more smoothly."

b. Make specific statements: "Lubricating bearings, races,
spindles, and knuckles will make the equipment operate
more smoothly."

c. Use an occasional negative statement: "The equipment
will not operate smoothly unless it is lubricated."

d. Make comparisons: "Lubricating will make the equipment operate more smoothly; failing to lubricate will
ruin it."

e. Use a prepositional beginning: "Without lubrication, the
equipment will operate badly."

f. Use a verbal beginning: "Lacking lubrication, the equipment will not operate smoothly."

g. Begin with a clause: "What the equipment needs for
smooth operation is good lubrication."

10. Have you avoided excessively long predicates?

A sense of movement within a paragraph is usually
achieved by the main verbs. Introducing additional verbs
in predicates may impede this movement. Therefore,
check the number of clauses in your predicates to see if
they can be reduced, or if the clauses can be changed to
phrases or verbals. For example:

The senator's fear was that if stocks became low, speculators
would enter the market and the price would be pushed up-
ward despite anything the SEC might try to do.

This statement contains five interlocked clauses, each
containing an important verb. The effect is unwieldy. It
could be easily revised to read with smoother Continuity:

The senator feared that low stocks would attract speculators
and start a rapid rise in prices despite any action by the SEC.

CHAPTER 8

Revising: Word Choice

Thus far we have been talking chiefly about the arrangement of words rather than about words themselves. Yet for most people, the biggest problem in writing is finding the right word. This is particularly true in any field demanding close attention to analysis, such as science, engineering, law. There is rarely a one-and-only right way to do things. The right way of saying something changes every time it is said. English is an especially idiomatic language, that is, it contains many words and phrases which could not be translated word for word into a foreign language and still make sense. But many of these phrases are illogical even for native speakers. For instance, we say, "put out the light," though most of us have not had candles or gaslight in our homes for years. If a logical-minded person were to try to eliminate idiomatic expressions of this kind, he might end up with something like "Extinguish the illumination," equally illogical and, what is worse, unnatural.

In Chapter 1 we discussed the point that language consists of music (idiom) as well as words. The music of the shop differs from the music of the drafting room, and the music of the drafting room differs from the music of the front office. Thus the language of reports constitutes a special problem: it must deal with complexities that often defy discussion and it must deal with them in different ways depending on whether the report is addressed to shop, drafting room, or front office. Approaching this problem with an ear to appropriateness—to subject, audi-

168

ence, purpose—is an easy way out. Complexity and simplicity after all are relative, and you will be pleasantly surprised to find how easy it is to play by ear when you put yourself in your reader's place, time, and circumstance.

Your ear would tell you, for example, which of these two versions would be better for a report addressed to a technical audience:

Under certain conditions of temperature and relative humidity, moisture content of the air increases oxidation of ferrous compounds.

Iron rusts.

When big words are needed to express big ideas to people who understand big words, big words are appropriate—even though they may be incomprehensible to outsiders. In fact, using shorter, nontechnical words may be confusing, ambiguous, or less accurate.

In general, then, when in Rome do as the Romans do. When writing to shop people use shop language. When writing to engineers, use engineering language. When writing to business people, use their language. But be professional: use your best manner of speaking and avoid weasel words, boasting, and pomposity as much as slang and cuss words. It is best to stick to standard professional language, assuming that any nonprofessional interested enough to read your report will use a dictionary. And once you have chosen a viewpoint, be consistent. Avoid, for instance, the change in viewpoint in the following excerpt:

The efficacy of hydrochloric acid is indisputable but the corrosive residue is incompatible with metallic permanence and eats hell out of lead pipes.

Check List for Word Choice

1. Have you used language attuned to subject?
   a. Avoided words more appropriate to talking than to writing?

> The drill worked swell.
> The new sealing compound is efficient but it stinks.

   b. Avoided discord?

> A mountain of shavings accumulated under the cutter as it galled, burned, and pooped out.
>
> The creative engineer without technical orientation deprives the Company of a vital gut.

   c. Avoided trite, overworked expressions and redundancy?

> The general consensus of opinion was that the sky's the limit.
>
> Mention of this was made to the customer in our last report for informational purposes.

   d. Avoided "literary" style, drawing attention away from the subject?

> The shavings burst into flames of brilliant orange and verdant green like a rainbow on a crystal clear day.

2. Have you used language attuned to audience?
   a. With respect to their status?

> *Not:* The plans you sent us weren't too good. Somebody in your office ought to write a book telling us how to read them. They call for junk we wouldn't be caught dead with.
>
> *But:* The plans are unacceptable because they do not meet our materials specification standards.

   b. With respect to their background?

> *Not:* (To mechanical engineers) We all know friction creates heat. Striking a match utilizes this principle, as does a Boy Scout starting a fire by twirling a stick against another piece of wood. The amount of heat created by automobile brakes in a fast stop from high speed is amazing.
>
> *But:* Assuming that a 100-horsepower vehicle requires 500-horsepower braking. . . .

   c. With respect to their intelligence?

Overexposure to radiation is a very serious problem. It can cause much damage, including death. Since the use of radioactive materials is becoming more common, the problem of safety is of great importance. Overexposure to radiation must be avoided.

Fifteen major deficiencies in the Army's new medium tank and a similar number in the new light tank were said to have been eliminated by engineering tests and changes in a report by the Army Chief of Staff.

d. With respect to their patience?

COMMUNICATION RESEARCH CO.
MEMORANDUM

NO. 7-11
DATE: 31 Sept 65

TO: Staff Officers
FROM: L. J. Mason
SUBJECT: Compliance

1. It has come to the attention of the undersigned that certain practices of the Staff appear under certain conditions to have created some comment upon these and perhaps upon others although as far as the latter is concerned this has not as yet been verified.

2. However, as a means of clarifying the situation, it is desired that all officers of the Corporation desist immediately from the practices alluded to except in cases where these appear necessary or perhaps desirable upon the understanding that while prior approval is always to be recommended it is not always possible.

3. In cases where action is indicated, responsible management are strictly enjoined to require compliance with Office Memorandum dated 4 July 1960, subject: "Compliance," which directs that all those who have not done so will do so immediately and that all who have two will turn one in.

LJM

3. Have you used language attuned to your purpose?

a. With respect to how it will be used? Whether the report is to be skimmed lightly, read for information, or studied carefully will determine these elements of style:

	Paragraphs	Sentences	Words	Details
SKIM	shortest	simple	nontechnical	summary tables labels
READ	medium	average	semitechnical	general
STUDY	longest	complex	technical	specific

FOR SKIMMING

An automated pancake-baking machine does everything but serve the customer. It turns out flapjacks or hot cakes at the rate of three a minute. The big griddle is shaped like a huge hour glass and pours batter, bakes one side, and turns the cake. It is designed for restaurants and hotels.

FOR READING

It will be noted during such experiments that the speaker occasionally hums and howls, sometimes to the point where the speaker fed by the microphone cannot be used in the same room. This is due to the acoustic and electrical coupling existing between both speakers. If the microphone speaker is taken to the far corner of the room or moved in different directions or sometimes even tilted horizontally, the howling may cease.

FOR STUDY[1]

The physical interpretation of change is as follows: Equation (4) states that the rate of momentum change for an element of fluid moving with the stream is equal to the sum of the forces due to pressure and viscous stresses on the surface of the element, and the forces due to fields acting throughout the interior. Equation (5) states that the internal energy of an element of fluid moving with the stream changes because of heat flow by conduction and radiation, work done against the surface forces, and work done by the force fields acting on the interior of the element. Equation (6) states that the mass fraction of component i is an element of fluid

[1] Slightly modified from: Warren E. Stewart, "The Wisconsin Course in Transport Phenomena," *Journal Engineering Education,* V (1959), 596.

moving at the mass average velocity v and changes because of diffusion and chemical reactions. . . .

b. With respect to what you hope to achieve?

  (1) *Telling.* The masterpiece of purposeful prose is Dr. Benjamin Spock's *Pocketbook of Baby and Child Care.* Its popularity rests largely on Dr. Spock's skill in telling a mother what to do before she has to do it, and telling her how to do it when she has to do it. He does this in such a way that even in the height of an emergency, the young mother remains calm, cool, and confident. The following passage discusses earache.

> Suppose it will be several hours before you can reach the doctor. What can you do to relieve the pain? [Note how the conversational tone conveys directions unhurriedly.] A hot-water bottle or an electric pad will help some. Small children are impatient of them. A few drops of warm oil in the ear is an old traditional remedy, but has little effect. (Don't ever put anything into an ear that is discharging, except when the doctor tells you to.) [Note the simple words and sentences for directness even at the expense of continuity.] A half tablet of aspirin for a small child, a full tablet (5 grains) for a child of six or more, will probably bring some relief. [Note the pacing—how information is introduced gradually.] What will help even more, if you happen to have it on hand, is a dose of cough medicine containing codeine that the doctor has prescribed for that particular child. (A medicine prescribed for an older child or adult might contain too much of the drug.) [Note how Dr. Spock treats the problem of using codeine—simply the use of the word "drug" warns against overuse.] Codeine is an efficient pain killer as well as cough medicine. If the earache is severe, you can use all these remedies together.

  (2) *Selling.* In the whole range of report writing perhaps no form comes closer to outright "selling" than proposals. These documents are intended to convince a customer that you can perform a given task better than anyone else could. The following example is an illustration of the kind of language appropriate to re-

ports of this type. (This is only a sample of the language, not of the scope or actual content a proposal would contain.)

Introduction

We would like to propose a program for the design specified in Letter AFBR 789-99. A detailed reference to the large number of similar programs we have managed would be beyond the scope of this proposal. We feel, however, that the experience gained from these programs places us in a strong position relative to our competitors.

Our competitors may have had many successes, but it should be pointed out that ours were on a larger and more impressive scale. Furthermore, we have a great deal of experience in specialty areas required for this partitcular design.

Capabilities

We have available all of the modern techniques of operational analysis and high-speed computing. These will be applied to the problem of efficiency optimization. It is expected that several nationally known consultants will be retained for this work because of the overriding importance of the problem.

Resources. An excellent survey of our physical facilities is contained in the attached auditor's report which was prepared during our most recent accounting.

Facilities. It is our belief that a project such as this should be carried out in our plant. We plan to use government-furnished facilities only if absolutely necessary.

4. Have you used language attuned to common usage?
   a. Have you avoided abused words?
      (1) *and etc. Etc.* means "and so forth," and so should not be preceded by *and.*
      (2) *appreciate, perfect, unique.* These words are absolutes, that is, there is no degree of "uniqueness" or "perfectness." Therefore, they should not be modified by words which express degree or comparison, such as *very, less, highly.*
      (3) *as—like.* In comparisons, *as* is a conjunction, that is, it is used before a clause, "The Solution looked as if

it had congealed." *Like* is a preposition, "The solution looked like coffee."

(4) *definitely.* *Definitely* means "clear-cut" or "in a definite manner." It is frequently misused in the sense of *certainly* or *surely.*

b. Have you avoided confused words?

(1) *accept—except.* *Accept* means "to agree to" or "to receive." *Except* means "to exclude" (as a verb) or "excluding" (as a preposition).

> When he accepted the assignment, everyone was pleased except his wife.

(2) *affect—effect.* *Affect* means "to influence" or "to put on airs." *Effect* means "to bring about or accomplish" (as a verb) or "result" (as a noun).

> Radiation affects health and so the AEC tries to effect safety programs at all installations. The effect is encouraging.

(3) *all ready—already.* *All ready* means that everything is completely ready. *Already* means "previously" or "by this time."

> The company is all ready for the program and has already begun overtime work.

(4) *continual—continuous.* *Continual* means "frequently repeated with intermittent breaks." *Continuous* means "uninterrupted continuity."

> Continuous eight-hour days would be tiring, so continual smoke-breaks have been introduced.

(5) *complement—compliment.* *Complement* means whatever completes. *Compliment* is praise.

> The Research Department received compliments for having complemented the work of the test lab.

(6) *definite—definitive.* *Definite* means "explicit, with clear outlines." *Definitive* means settling something absolutely or finally.

There is a definite need for a definitive statement on pricing policies.

(7) *infer—imply*. *Infer* means "to draw a conclusion" or "judge from the evidence." *Imply* means "to hint, suggest, or insinuate."

He inferred from the data that the price was too high, but implied that he would accept the estimate anyway.

(8) *its—it's*. *Its* means "belonging to it." *It's* is the contraction of "it is."

It's up to the Department to settle its own problems.

(9) *Lay—lie*. *Lay* means "to put down." *Lie* (in this sense) means to be down already.

He laid down a program for strong action but it will lie around the Director's office for six months. Last year Jones laid down a similar program and it has lain there all this time.

(10) *leave—let*. *Leave* means "to depart." *Let* means "to permit, allow."

Please let us leave this boiler factory.

(11) *liable—likely*. *Liable* means "legally responsible" or indicates probability of something unpleasant happening. *Likely* can mean "expected" or "probable."

The Contractor is liable for shortages but they are not likely in these days of close control? That's a likely story!

(12) *percent—percentage*. *Percent* follows a numeral in formal writing. *Percentage* is the more usual form without numerals.

Reject rates fell off 46 percent, a remarkable percentage.

(13) *practical—practicable*. *Practical* means "useful" or "sensible." *Practicable* means "possible," "usable," "capable of being done," but never applies to persons.

Practical people often have practicable plans.

(14) *principal—principle. Principal* is an adjective meaning "chief," "primary," "major" (except the principal of a school). *Principle* is a noun meaning "law," "rule," "doctrine."

> The principal reason for the change is the principle that the trouble with industry is people.

(15) *raise—rise. Raise* means "to lift." *Rise* means "to be lifted."

> With a raise in salary, performance will rise.

(16) *there—their—they're. There* means "in that place." *Their* means "belonging to them." *They're* is the contraction of "they are."

> They're supposed to put their signatures there on the dotted line.

(17) *use—utilize. Use* means "to employ something." *Utilize* (a formal word) means "to put to use."

> We use the semi-omega approach and utilize a lead pencil.

(18) *which—that. Which* usually introduces clauses that are nonrestrictive (unnecessary to main sense). *That* introduces restrictive clauses (necessary to the main sense).

> The plan that they followed, which has already been discussed, succeeded where others failed.

(19) *where—when. Where* indicates place. *When* indicates time.

> When a component fails, the contractor is liable except where state laws prohibit such agreements.

(20) *who—which—that. Who* refers to people. *Which* refers to things. *That* may refer to persons or things.

> Who knows which factory produces parts that never fail?

c. Have you avoided misused words?

    (1) *ability—capacity. Ability* refers to power to perform. *Capacity* is power to receive or hold.

        His ability to drink is limited by his capacity.

    (2) *alternate—alternative.* Alternate can mean either "substitution" or "occurrence in turn." *Alternative* means a choice between two possibilities.

        Alternate delegates have no alternative to being on call.

    (3) *among—between. Among* refers to more than two. *Between* refers to two.

        Among the salesmen there is no distinction between traveling and selling from the floor.

    (4) *amount—number. Amount* is used for an aggregate. *Number* is used for a quantity that cannot be counted now.

        He had a large amount of money stored in a number of banks around the country.

    (5) *apparent—evident—obvious. Apparent* means "perceived by the senses" (or "seeming"). *Evident* means "accepted as true." *Obvious* means "so plain it cannot be missed."

        Although your intention is apparent, your logic is not evident, and so the point is not obvious at all.

    (6) *fewer—less. Fewer* applies to numbers. *Less* applies to amount or degree.

        The fewer the people, the less the noise.

    (7) *former—latter. Former* refers to the first of two. *Latter* refers to the second of two.

        In comparing nuclear and electrical propulsion, consider the former in terms of necessary precautions and the latter in terms of development costs.

    (8) *past—last. Past* refers to what has gone by. *Last* usually refers to the end of the line.

In the past month we completed the last of the T-4-2 models.

(9) *thereby—therefore. Thereby* means "by that means." *Therefore* means "for that reason" or "consequently."

He increased the pressure, thereby placing too much strain on the old pump. Therefore, he had to install a new pump.

(10) *which.* As a pronoun, *which* must refer to something and must be placed close to its antecedent.

Not: The Comptroller conducted an investigation from his office which disclosed grave discrepancies.
But: From his office the Comptroller conducted an investigation which disclosed . . .

After you have examined the report for accuracy, continuity, and appropriate language, two more steps remain: (1) read the document aloud—or have someone read it to you; and (2) proofread. Reading the report aloud will let you hear for yourself how smoothly and easily it flows along. Careful proofreading will ensure the impression that you cared enough about the work to make the copy as accurate as possible. Your best tool for this purpose is a good dictionary, such as *Webster's New Collegiate Dictionary,* the *American College Dictionary,* or the *New World Dictionary.* An unabridged dictionary is particularly helpful for checking word usage as well as spelling, meaning, and pronunciation. You will find that a good dictionary also has chapters devoted to language history, punctuation, and other helpful information (statistics, foreign phrases, etc.), including proofreading tips.

PRACTICE PROBLEMS: REVISING

The following passages are to be revised to meet the indicated requirements of audience and purpose:

1. Sell the product to photo hobbyists:

Is Tradition of Any Value?

Since more than a hundred years in the heart of Europe in the nice Thuringian city of Jena are manufactured fine-mechanical and optical ground instruments of high precision. Thousands of workmen of the giant works of Jena are proud of this tradition. It spurs them to always outstanding performances. That is the real value of this tradition.

A Miniature Camera with a Great Future

The world-renowned Jena works making use of their valuable experiences in the past and foreseeing the requirements of the future have designed the Miniature Camera WHOO. The Camera has its name from the Whoo river rising in the Thuringian Woods. This camera of highest precision shows an outstanding design and excellent workmanship brought to a perfect maturity in many decades. This is also the special value of this tradition.

May Easily Be Sold

The WHOO realizes the dream of a camera. Nothing has been disregarded. The result: The WHOO Camera owing to its special look units keenest price with greatest reliability—it gives to its owner just what the large and pretentious amateur circles wish to possess. Below we give you the most important sale's features:

Coated lens—Original Jena T-2.8/50 mm

Three point focusing, highest definitive power

Outstanding color correction

Synchro-Compur shutter—1/500 sec., incorporated automatic release

Rapid winding by 1/6 rotation of the large front ring; Optimistic feature

Unequalled refinement with simultaneously sturdy design

Universally applicable shutter cap (as counter light diaphragm —filters may be set in)

Quite original film stage assures absolutely plane position

WHOO—THE DREAM OF A CAMERA WITH SPECIAL LOOK

2. Define the problem for top management review and program approval:

Since compactness is most important in electronics equipments, many new components have been developed such as transistors, polyethylene capacitors, miniature transformers, and many small components. When working with these new components, care must be taken so as not to heat or melt them while soldering into place. If a faster-drying metallic cement could be found much time could be saved in construction of equipments. This construction is now being done by hand with low-wattage soldering irons, which is difficult.

3. Inform management:

Certain components of the electronic equipment carried by missiles are subject to failure at relatively low temperatures, while the skin temperature of a missile is relatively high. For a missile traveling at Mach 5 (10,000 feet altitude), the skin temperature reaches 760°F. After steady-state conditions are reached, the interior of the missile would be near or at skin temperature. The rocket motor would be at much higher temperature. Certain of the electronic components generate high temperatures of their own. These conditions necessitate cooling equipment for the electronic equipment to insure against electronic failure.

4. Recommend to specialists:

Over-all results seem to indicate that mechanically (possibly because of a simpler mechanism) the Alphaalpha units are superior to the Betabeta units. Actually there was only one positively identified outright mechanical failure. This occurred in an Alphaalpha unit when a contact spring broke during life tests. Betabeta units performed very badly under saltspray tests. On both units, excellent sealing qualities were afforded by the rubber seals.

5. Give management quick information about the situation:

Contractor's experience to date indicates that it is feasible to extend to 6 months the 60-day limit for storage of zootrons without exercising. This will incur no significant increase in the risk of zootron failure. Both the completion of Contract 1234 and the scheduled 30 June delivery will make available tactical transmitter-receiver test equipment before the six-month zootron-storage limit has elapsed. Therefore it is not believed necessary to provide a zootron conditioner for zootrons in storage. Zootrons which have not been exercised for 6 months may be returned for conditioning on special equipment which increases voltage to the zootron in programmed stages.

6. Give engineers quick information about the problem:

Aeromedical researchers believe that man will be able to take long space flights. They realize, however, that man is a captive of his environment and that the human organism cannot live apart from this environment. In order for man to travel the planetary route, the designer of vehicles for outer space travel must assure him of the comforts and familiar aspects of the earth's environment during space flight. The members of space ship crews will undergo a thorough screening process in order to be capable of handling any emergency. Each crew member will be subjected to a battery of psychological tests that would have indicated the adapability of each member to endure the hazards of space travel. These are: weightlessness, buffeting, acceleration, deceleration, exposure to cosmic radiation, cold, heat, isolation, and the vibration of re-entry into the earth's atmosphere. Experiments have shown that music has been a deterrent to boredom, thereby taped music will be available at all stations aboard the ship. The space vehicle must be designed in such a way that man will be able to survive for long periods of time with some degree of safety.

7. Inform shop mechanics about the process:

A preliminary investigation shows that two methods of conveying electrical test data from the accelerometer turntable to the accelerometer turntable stand are possible:

Method 1. Bring the accelerometer lead to the center of the turntable. Connect the lead to the swivel which has complete electrical contact. Extend the swivel end of the lead perpendicular to the turntable a distance far enough so that test accelerometers clear the lead. Convey the lead to the edge of the accelerometer turntable stand where it can be connected to an electrical outlet.

Method 2. Bring accelerometer lead to center of turntable. Extend lead down center of turntable shaft to shaft attachment. From shaft attachment electrical data will be picked up by brushes riding on shaft attachment and conveyed to accelerometer turntable stand where lead can be attached to an electrical outlet.

Method 2 must be used because it enables the operator to close the protective top during operation. The only problem involved in using this method is the design and cost of the shaft attachment. There are three types of shaft attachments to be considered. They are the tapped shaft attachment, the external clamp, and the internal clamp. Investigations are being made considering each of these attachments for strength, cost of design, cost of installation, and maintenance.

8. Analyze this situation for management:

It would be advisable to isolate, or divorce in some fashion, the work being done by personnel classified within our new factory schedule. Otherwise, it is entirely conceivable that strong attempts will be made to unionize departments where coexistence has been established. The orbits of coercive comparison—those workers classified under the old structure and those classified under the new—may, conversely, in areas where workers are integrated, set into movement the forces of attrition at an extremely undesirable level.

Essentially, it is recognized as the type of situation that might shovel a steady and highly conflagrant grade of coal to the fire of an organization attempt. And worthy of consideration is the fact that should attrition be "induced," or "encouraged," at levels falling within the old classifications, we are faced with only two alternative courses of action. They may simply quit, or they may remain within the Company. If an employee quits he will be pointed out as an illustrative example of gross injustice. If he remains, internal problems are propagated, and the cycle remains in motion.

9. Thank the customer:

REDBALL ROCKET COMPANY
Skyhook Lane
Cleveland 6

1 April 1964

Transcendent Airlines
New York 72, New York

Gentlemen:

The writer wishes to thank you for placing your recent order for twenty-five space ships, Model 7-QRS-2, with our company. Please be assured that we are now reviewing all your specs which you indicated on your order as we have a sincere and earnest desire to give you satisfaction.

May I tell you that we shall undertake everything possible within our power to try and be of assistance or service to you now and in the future as a convenient and ready source of supply whenever you are in the market.

In addition, please permit me to state that we shall always welcome any suggestion or comments that you may care to make relative to any and all methods of improvement of our service to you or any of our countless thousands of other happy and satisfied customers.

In the meantime, if you should be in Cleveland, do not hesitate to drop in whenever you think that there is something in the way of which we can be of help or further assistance to you and yours.

Your friendly
REDBALL ROCKET COMPANY

George Atkinson
President

CHAPTER 9

Revising: Mechanics

For those of us who can never remember whether it is "*i* before *e* except after *c*" or the other way around, this chapter condenses in simplified form some current practices in common reports, particularly those in science and industry. Topics covered are: (1) punctuation, (2) spelling, (3) abbreviation, (4) capitalization, (5) footnoting, (6) heading, (7) using figures for numbers, (8) paging, (9) using units of measure and symbols.

1. PUNCTUATION

The Period

1. Used at the end of a sentence or completed expression.

   Work stopped.   No.

2. Used after general abbreviations, but not after many technical abbreviations. (See abbreviations.)

   Mr., Mrs., Dr., A.M.
   Cu, psi, g

3. Used before a decimal.

   $16.63; 0.0025

The Comma

1. Sets off words, phrases, and clauses not essential to the meaning.

The program, outlined below, is known as a crash task.

2. Sets off introductory phrases and clauses to avoid confusion.

    As soon as she started eating, her dog choked on a bone.

3. Sets off words that modify the whole sentence.

    The package, finally, will be flight-tested.

4. Separates items in series.

    There was a document signed by Roosevelt, Stalin, and Churchill.

5. Separates distinct, closely related ideas.

    The project was discontinued, but the contractor reimbursed us for all expenses incurred.

6. Sets off *however, nevertheless,* and *therefore* when used for connection or to modify a whole sentence. (These words should be preceded by a semicolon, however, when they introduce a clause. Note the difference between the second and third examples below.)

    The question, therefore, is open.
    He is lazy; however, he is honest. (*Or* He is lazy. However, he is honest.)
    He is lazy, however, and must be fired.

7. Used before and after *namely, that is* (*i.e.*), and *for example* (*e.g.*) when introducing examples. (Note: i.e. and e.g. are not italic.)

    The aim is the same, i.e., to make money.

8. Used any time to avoid confusion.

    Friday the plumber said he would come to fix the sink.
    Friday, the plumber, said he would come to fix the sink.
    Friday, the plumber said, he would come to fix the sink.

9. Remember to close off unessential or parenthetical phrases and clauses with a second comma.

    Mort Stein, our representative, is here.

The Semicolon

1. Used between parts of a compound sentence (between independent clauses) when they are not connected by a conjunction.

   The level rose and fell; the pressure remained constant.
   The level rose and fell, but the pressure remained constant.

2. Used between independent clauses connected by words such as: then, however, moreover, nevertheless, furthermore, thus, consequently. (Note these adverbs are not considered conjunctions.)

   He failed at everything; nevertheless, he kept trying.

3. Separates members of a series of clauses or phrases if one or more of the clauses or phrases contain a comma.

   Foremen include Art Barney, Shop 306; Jack Berg, Shop 411; and Al White, Shop 907.

The Colon

1. Introduces a formal enumeration.

   The parts are as follows:

2. Used after salutations in letters.

   Gentlemen: Dear Sir:

3. Used to separate parts of ratios.

   12:19   X:57

4. Used to separate hour and minutes in writing nonmilitary time.

   1:30 P.M.   12:01 A.M.

The Dash

1. Used to separate and give emphasis to an element of a sentence.

   Take these prints away—and burn them.

2. Used to separate a parenthetical insertion which defines, enumerates, or explains a phrase in the main clause.

These machines—linotype, monotype, binder, and press—are essential in producing a book.

Parentheses

1. Used to set off information not essential to meaning.

This fabric (in a variety of colors) is available for Model 768.

2. Used to set off references from the rest of the text.

Ratings are expected to rise higher in the coming year. (See Chapter 7.)

3. If statement is independent of sentence, parenthesis is outside the punctuation.

Strength depends on many factors. (Since these factors are not relevant, they are omitted here.)

If statement is pertinent to a sentence, parenthesis is inside the punctuation of the sentence.

Strength depends on a number of factors (material, structure, weight, and so forth).

Brackets

1. Used for parentheses within parentheses.

The program closed (after six months [January-June]) for lack of funds.

2. Used to indicate an insertion in quoted material.

"He [Jones] would sign it," said the president.

The Hyphen

1. Use hyphens in compound words whenever their omission would result in ambiguity.

The twin-engine trainer is ideal for low-level interception practice.

2. Hyphenate fractions when the numerator and denominator are both one-word forms, but do not use hyphen between the numerator and denominator if either numerator or denominator contains a hyphen.

    one-third   four thirty-seconds
    three-sixteenths

3. Hyphenate compound adjectives when they precede the noun they modify, but not when they follow the noun.

    the well-informed manager   the manager was well informed

4. Do not hyphenate compounds of adverb and adjective where no ambiguity might result. Do not hyphenate a compound containing an -ly adverb.

    privately owned   ever increasing sales
    highly developed program

5. Do not hyphenate prefixes such as non, sub, inter, pre, etc. Exceptions: if prefixes are followed by a proper noun or a hyphenated expression; if omitting the hyphen would result in a double vowel (aa, ii, for example); if omitting the hyphen changes the meaning of the word.

    nonrevenue   un-ionized (unionized)
    non-revenue-producing   interoffice
    re-evaluate   inter-American
    re-sign (resign)

6. Hyphenate terms of two or more words when they have the meaning of one thought.

    cost-plus-fixed-fee   tungsten-inert-gas
    stress-strain

7. Hyphenate units of double measurement.

    watt-hour   man-hour

2. SPELLING

1. Here are the ten word groups most frequently misspelled:

their, there, they're	definite, definitely, definition,
two, too, to	define
receive, receiving, received	separate, separation
exist, existence, existent	believe, belief
occur, occurred, occurring,	occasion, occasionally
occurrence	lose, losing

2. These words are frequently misspelled through carelessness:

affect, effect	precede, proceed, procedure
category	than, then
comparative	through, thorough
consistent, consistency	weather, whether
height	passed, past
interpret	varies, various

3. These words are frequently misspelled through doubt:

choose, chose, choosing	exaggerate
control, controlling,	unnecessary
controlled	recommend
embarrass	shining

3. ABBREVIATION

1. Use abbreviations in the singular.
2. Ordinarily use small letters except when abbreviating capitalized words, such as British thermal unit (Btu), Fahrenheit (F), Centigrade (C). ID (inside diameter) and OD (outside diameter) are exceptions.
3. Abbreviate common units of weights and measures *when they follow numerals.* Modern usage prefers, however, that units of weights and measures be spelled out in the text.
4. Abbreviate and capitalize "number" when it precedes a numeral as in "No. 3."

TABLE VI. Trouble-Shooting Spelling

Problem	Instance	Rule/Recommendation	Remarks	Examples
Carelessness	*resistent* for *resistant*	Try to pronounce a word correctly. Distinguish between root (base of word) and prefix or suffix (syllable attached to root to change meaning or function). Proofread.	When in doubt, look it up.	*devellop* for *develop* *visable* for *visible* *desireable* for *desirable* *duely* for *duly*
Confusion	*affect* for *effect*	Try visualizing the difference between words of similar sound and memorizing the difference in meaning.	Maybe you can think of some memory devices, e.g., "*a* before *e*, so you affect an effect."	*accept—except* *advice—advise* *choose—chose* *forward—foreword* *led—lead* *loose—lose* *passed—past* *stationary—stationery*
i before *e*?	*believe* for *believe*	If the sound is *ee* (relief), use *ie* — except after *c* (receive); if the sound is *a* (neighbor), use *ei*.	Common exceptions are either, neither, leisure, and seize.	*believe* *ceiling* *weigh*
Drop the *e*?	*writing* for *writing*	Drop final *e* before a suffix beginning with a vowel. Keep it before a suffix beginning with a consonant.	Words ending in *ce* or *ge* keep the *e* before suffixes beginning with *a* or *o*; as in *noticeable, manageable,* and *advantageous.*	*change—changing* *move—movement, moving* *ice—icy* *safe—safely*
Double the letter?	*occured* for *occurred*	When adding a suffix beginning with a vowel, double the consonant for all one-syllable words and for words of more than one syllable accented on the last syllable, when the word ends in a single consonant, preceded by a single vowel.	An interesting exception is gases. Note if the accent shifts to an earlier syllable when the ending is added, the final consonant is not doubled.	*referred* *redder* *lagging* *controlling* *reference* *admittance*

5. Some common abbreviations

amp	ampere	in.-lb	inch-pound
ac	alternating current	ipm	inches per minute
cc	cubic centimeter	ipr	inches per revolution
cfm	cubic feet per minute	ipt	inches per tooth
cfs	cubic feet per second	kv	kilovolt
cm	centimeter	log	logarithm
cu ft	cubic foot	psf	pounds per square foot
cu in.	cubic inch	psi	pounds per square inch
ft-lb	foot pound	psig	pounds per square inch, gage
gpm	gallons per minute	Rb	Rockwell hardness "B"

4. CAPITALIZATION

1. Capitalize the first word in a sentence.
2. Capitalize principal words in titles:

> Technical Order 2B-52D-4-U
> Specification MIL-o-67890
> *Maintenance of Skyhooks*

3. Capitalize proper nouns, abbreviations of proper nouns, and words derived from proper nouns except those that have been used so frequently that they are now considered common nouns.

Allison engine	diesel engine
Fahrenheit	watt
Van Allen belt	mach number
Mach 2.5	pasteurize
British	scotch plaid

4. Capitalize points of the compass when identifying specific areas, but do not capitalize nouns simply designating direction.

Middle West	west of the Mississippi
Southeast Asia	a southeasterly direction

6. REFERENCES

Footnotes must be used when quoting directly from a published source and to acknowledge sources of paraphrased material. They may also be used to acknowledge indebtedness for assistance. They should seldom be used in a report to add further information or explanation. This material should be integrated with the text or, if it is too long and would destroy continuity, it should be placed in an appendix.

References are generally supplied in three ways.

1. A footnote number in the text may refer to a note containing full bibliographical information.[1] The note may appear at the foot of the page or at the end of a chapter or report.
2. Notes may be used to refer to a numbered entry on the reference page or in the bibliography.[2] Specific page numbers are sometimes included in this type of note.[3]
3. A number in parentheses in the text line may refer to a numbered entry in the bibliography. Or, the author's name and the date of publication may be supplied in the text, with full publishing information in the bibliography.

Footnote numbers are superscripts without brackets or punctuation. Arabic numerals are used in consecutive series. Symbols, such as * or †, may be used when there are very few notes and are always used in mathematical material to avoid confusion with superscript numbers. Italic letters or symbols may be used for notes to tables.

Footnote form varies widely, but basic patterns are given below.

Reference to Book
Claude D. Frank, *Toroballistics,* 2nd ed., New York: Keynote Press, 1894, p. 309.
Claude D. Frank, ed., *Anthology of Toroballistics* ("College Text Series"), New York: Cramden Company, 1942, chaps. 1, 3-5.

Reference to a Journal
Claude D. Frank, "Variables in Toroballistics," *Production Planning,* XVI (July, 1957), 306-307.

[1] Claude D. Frank, *Toroballistic Theory,* 4th ed., New York: Prudent Press, 1906, p. 18.
[2] Reference 16.
[3] Reference 16, p. 76.

Reference to a Magazine
Claude D. Frank, "The Computer and I," *Reader's Review,* July, 1957, pp. 23-24.

Reference to a Report
Claude D. Frank, Toroballistic Parameters, Jones & Stell Company, R-643, 1956.

Reference to a Newspaper
Claude D. Frank, "Letter to the Editor," *New Amsterdam News,* July 4, 1957, p. C5.

Reference to Unpublished Material
Claude D. Frank in private correspondence (or interview, etc.), July 4, 1957.

The following are acceptable shortcuts in footnotes.

For a work previously cited: Frank, *Toroballistics,* p. 28.
For a work cited in the immediately preceding note: *Ibid.,* p. 29, or Frank, p. 29.
Author's first name may be omitted or abbreviated.
Title may be abbreviated, especially titles of well-known periodicals.
Words "volume" and "page" may be omitted.

The following are acceptable abbreviations in footnotes:

ch., chs. (or chap.)	chapter, chapters
col., cols.	column, columns
ed.	editor, edited by, edition
f., ff.	the following page, the following pages
p., pp.	page, pages
rev.	revised
trans.	translated by

The following are acceptable forms for bibliographies:

Books with One or More Authors
Alfred, J. B., D. C. Courant, and R. L. Clock. *Industrial Plastics.* New York: Wiley, 1960.
Olsen, J. A. *Materials Processing.* New York: Harper, 1959.
Wrandt, F. C. *Refinery Plant Design.* 2nd ed. New York: Petroleum Institute, 1960.

Edited Books
Gaylord, H. E., and Rubin Schwartz, eds. *Pricing Yearbook*. Chicago: Pricing Research Bureau, 1961.
Modern Housekeeping Practices. Ed. Modern Housekeeping Staff. New York: Modern Housekeeping Magazine, 1958-1960. 3 vols.
Walters, J. H., ed. *Milling Handbook*. Philadelphia: University of Pennsylvania Press, 1960.

Chart or Table in a Book
"Flow Rates in Hydraulic Reservoirs," in *Hydraulics Handbook*. 4th ed. New York: Harper, 1960.

Periodicals, No Particular Article
Product Engineering. 1950–1961
Wall Street Journal. 1950–1961.

Periodical Articles with Authors
Alden, R. C., "Conversion of Hydrozine to Liquid Fuel," *Petroleum Production*, XXV (January, 1960), 130-136.
Alden, R. C., and James B. Harris, "Appraisal of Gas Pockets," *Proceedings of the American Gas Institute*, III (1965), 425, 480, 489-497.

Periodical Articles Without Authors
"Dehydrating Concrete," *Highway Engineering*, VIII (November, 1955), 120-137.

Several Documents by Same Author
Abrahams, J. R., and Braunell Wexler. "Light Hydrocarbon Liquids." *Petroleum Notes and Queries*, 2nd series, XX (1950), 23-24.
———. "Light Hydrocarbon Liquids Once More." *Petroleum Notes and Queries*, 2nd series, XXI (1951), 304.
———. *Manual of Hydrocarbon Liquids*. New York: Jones Press, 1960.

Government Publications
Tennessee Valley Authority, Engineering Division. *Status Report on Engineering Activities*. Washington, 1963.
U.S. Bureau of the Census. *Survey of Current Business*. Washington, 1960.

Business Publication with Corporate Author
Boeing Airplane Company. *Sealing*. Seattle, 1957.

Lemon Growers Federation. *Seven Ways to Health.* Los Angeles, 1960.
Series
Heilbrunner, A. J. *Oliver Evans* ("American Engineering History Society Monographs," No. 14.) Los Angeles: Poverty Press, 1960.

6. HEADINGS

Use of headings is dictated by whether the report is to be skimmed, read, or studied. A report for skimming should feature many headings; a report to be studied requires fewer. The example below is designed for skimming. The example on p. 197 is designed for studying.

STABILITY OF EPOXY RESIN MASTER GAUGES	Title
IV TEST ANALYSIS	Main head
A. Types of Movement	Subhead
Two types of movement occurred in the gauge: (1) expansion and (2) contraction.	
1. Expansion	Second
Linear measurements between relatively distant points showed no measurable elongation until stiffeners were removed. Then. . . .	subhead
2. Contraction	
When the stiffeners were removed shrinkage prevented the gauge from staying in plane. Its stability was. . . .	
B. Warpage	

7. USING FIGURES FOR NUMBERS

1. Any number is written out when it begins a sentence.

   Ten thousand Frenchmen can't be wrong.

2. Numbers up to and including ten are written out, except:
   a. When given for reference or calculation:

      Order 6 at $4.98 each.

   b. When used with numbers above ten in the same passage:

      We will buy 5 tables, 16 desks, and 21 chairs.

3. Round numbers expressing approximate figures or indefinite quantities are written out.

   about ten or twelve
   nearly a million kva

4. When two numbers refer to one item, the first number is usually spelled out. It is becoming common practice, however, to write out the smaller of the two.

> six 6-inch boards
> one 6-volt battery
> 12 one-volt batteries

PREPARATION OF TYPESCRIPT

GENERAL

Rough draft copy for typists should be double spaced, with triple spaces between paragraphs. A triple space should separate the last line of any paragraph from either a main head or first subhead. Left-hand margins should be about 3/4 inch and right-hand margins about 1/2 inch. Pages should be numbered in the center at the bottom of the first page, and in the upper right-hand corner of succeeding pages.

HEADINGS

Seven weights of headings should be used. The title is typed in the top center of the first page and is underlined. All other headings are also underlined. All letters of the main headings are capitalized. They are not indented. The first word of a paragraph is indented five spaces.

First Subhead

The first subhead capitalizes only initial letters of words over four letters long, is not indented, and is placed above the text.

SECOND SUBHEAD. The second subhead has all letters capitalized and is indented five spaces. It is run into the text, separated by double spacing. The text following the head runs to the left- and right-hand margins.

Third Subhead. The third subhead and its text follow the same pattern as the second subhead except that only initial letters of words over four letters long are capitalized.

FOURTH SUBHEAD. The fourth subhead looks like the second subhead but the text following it is indented five spaces from the lefthand margin.

Fifth Subhead. The fifth subhead is like the third subhead but the text following it, like that following the fourth subhead, is indented five spaces from the left-hand margin.

5. Fractions are written out when they stand alone, but are expressed in figures when used with units of measurement.

> one-half of all our acreage
> ½ gal.
> ³⁄₁₆ in.

6. All units of measurement are given as figures, including time, distance, weight, etc.

> 4:32 P.M.   5 ft
> 0900 hrs   6 min
> 16 lbs

7. Figures are also required for:

Street addresses	1901 Beech Street
Dates	3 June 1909, or June 3, 1909
Money	$25.00 (but $20 billion)
Page numbers	page 63
Illustration numbers	Figure 6
Table numbers	Table VI
Percentages	6 percent, or 6%

8. PAGING

1. Two common systems of paging are acceptable:
   a. Use arabic numerals throughout; or
   b. Use lower case roman numerals (i, ii, iii, iv, etc.) for prefatory material, such as the foreword or summary page.
2. The title page is not numbered but is considered to be the first page (1 or i). Except for the first page of text (usually the introduction), pages are numbered in the upper right-hand corner, 1/2 inch from the top, 2 inches from the right-hand side (not margin) of the paper. Often the word "page" is used. On the first page of the text the number will appear centered, 1/2 inch from the bottom of the paper.
3. Page consecutively throughout the report. Do not begin a new sequence of numbers with a new chapter.
4. Running titles are not necessary on each page when the report is numbered. The report number appears in the upper

right-hand corner of each page, a single space above the page number. If the report is unnumbered, an abbreviated title may be used in the upper left-hand corner, parallel to the page number and aligned with left-hand margin of the text.

9. USING UNITS OF MEASURE AND SYMBOLS

1. Use singular forms if number is 1 or less:

1 inch	3 inches
0.75 inch	1.025 inches
0.5 pound	5 pounds
1 g	3 g's

2. Do not repeat units with each of a series of numbers:

6 by 12 by 24 inches	increments of 15, 32, and 64
100 to 150 percent	degrees
60 to 90 degree angle	190-240°F.

3. Tolerances may be expressed as follows:

$$+ 0.003 \qquad 2.250 \pm 0.125$$
$$0.050$$
$$- 0.000$$
$$0.050 + 0.003, -0.000$$
$$0.050 + 0.003/ -0.000$$

4. Symbols other than math or chemical symbols are ordinarily not used in the text, such as:

/	per	"	inch
#	pound (after the word)	'	foot
#	number (before the word)	x	by

Recommended Reading

Emberger, M. E., and M. R. Hall. *Scientific Writing.* New York: Harcourt, Brace, 1955. This is a full discussion of problems in scientific and technical writing, amply illustrated.

Evans, Bergen, and Cornelia Evans. *Contemporary American Usage.* New York: Random House, 1957. This dictionary discusses ways and means of expression and compares American and British usage. If it interests you, you may want to go on to Donald J. Lloyd and Harry Warfel, *American English in Its Cultural Settings* (New York: Knopf, 1956). The old standard for this kind of book is H. L. Mencken, *The American Language* (4th ed. New York: Knopf, 1936 and supplements).

Fowler, H. W. *Modern English Usage.* New York: Oxford Press, 1952. Although concerned with British usage, this book should be in every writer's library. It is a sensible and entertaining dictionary of troublesome expressions, usage, and habits.

Godfrey, J. W., and Geoffrey Parr. *The Technical Writer.* New York: Wiley, 1959. This book is intended for the professional technical writer and covers everything from schematics to reproduction processes in color.

Gunning, Robert. *The Technique of Clear Writing.* New York: McGraw-Hill, 1952. This book is intended for writers in business and journalism, but it is also very helpful for anyone who would like to develop a modern, clean, brisk prose style.

Kapp, R. O. *The Presentation of Technical Information.* New York: Macmillan, 1957. This excellent short discussion of techniques for presenting complex, technical information was meant for a British audience, but its counsel on organization, pacing, and simplification are very valuable to anyone who must handle technical information in writing or in speeches.

Lee, Irving J. *Language Habits in Human Affairs*. New York: Harper, 1941. This book and any of the several books by S. I. Hayakawa will serve as good introductions to principles and applications of semantics in report writing and everyday life.

Lutz, R. H. *Graphic Presentation Simplified*. New York: Funk and Wagnalls, 1949. A helpful book on preparing charts, graphs, and other illustrations.

A Manual of Style. 11th ed. Chicago: University of Chicago Press, 1949.

Masterson, J. R., and W. B. Phillips. *Federal Prose*. Chapel Hill: University North Carolina Press, 1948. This is a very funny and informative book about the way government documents are written—or rather *were* written before the book was published.

Melcher, D., and Nancy Larrick. *Printing and Promotion Handbook*. New York: McGraw-Hill, 1956. This encyclopedia covers such topics as layout, typography, printing, and similarly helpful information for professional writers, publishers, and public relations people.

Murphey, R. W. *How and Where to Look It Up*. New York: McGraw-Hill, 1958. This is a helpful guide to standard sources of information in practically any field you can think of.

Perrin, P. G. *Writer's Guide and Index to English*. 3rd ed. Chicago: Scott-Foresman, 1959. After many years this still remains the best of the handbooks for composition, perhaps chiefly because of the very helpful index of problem areas that constitutes half the book.

Product Engineering Staff. Reading, Writing, Reporting. New York: Product Engineering (Reader Service Department, 330 West 42 Street, New York 36), 1960. This booklet of 24 pages offers a quick and easy summary of tips on reading, writing, and speaking for the working engineer.

Sherwood, John. *Discourse of Reason*. New York: Harper, 1960. This is a brief, readable discussion of logic and semantics applicable to writing. It is much shorter and less detailed than another text covering the same ground—Monroe C. Beardsley. *Thinking Straight* (2nd ed. Edgewood Cliffs, N.J.: Prentice-Hall, 1956).

Sigband, Norman B. *Effective Report Writing*. New York: Harper, 1960. This book is a complete text on business reports, including methods of compiling information, organizing, and presenting appropriate data.

Skillin, M. E., R. M. Gay, and others. *Words into Type*. New York: Appleton-Century-Crofts, 1948. This is a compendium of helpful information for preparing typescripts for the press.

The Society of Technical Editors and Publishers, P.O. Box 3706, Beachwold Station, Columbus 14, Ohio, publishes a bibliography of technical writing.

Strunk, William, and E. B. White. *Elements of Style*. New York: Macmillan, 1959. This little book is deservedly a best seller because of its brisk, no-nonsense approach and very brief format. For a more detailed and modern approach to grammar based on findings of recent work in linguistics, philosophy, physics, and psychology, see Paul Roberts, *Understanding English* (New York: Harper, 1958). A more specialized treatment of modern linguistics is James Sledd, *A Short Introduction to English Grammar* (Chicago: Scott-Foresman, 1959).

Turabian, Kate L. *Manual for Writers of Term Papers, Theses and Dissertations*. Chicago: University of Chicago Press, 1955.

Ulman, Joseph N., Jr. *Technical Reporting*. New York: Holt, 1952. This book was revised in 1959, by Jay R. Gould, to include more material. It remains one of the best on the subject, covering enormous territory in brief, brisk style.

United States Government Printing Office. *Plain Letters* and *The GPO Manual of Style*. Two very helpful books for report writers.

Upton, Albert. *Design for Thinking: A First Book in Semantics*. 7th Experimental Edition. Whittier, Calif.: Whittier College, 1959. Although, at this time, Professor Upton's book is not yet generally available it is obtainable from Whittier College where it is used as a basic text in psychosemantics and has proved very effective in enabling Whittier students to raise IQ test scores remarkably.

Worthing, Archie, and J. Geffner. *Treatment of Experimental Data*. New York: Wiley, 1943. This is a very helpful book, not only for its stated subject but also for its tips on preparing charts, graphs, and other illustrations.

Index